DIAGNOSTICS BASED UPON OBSERVATION OF PALMAR LINES
——Chinese Palmistry in Medical Application

Written by   Wang Chenxia

Illustrated by   Da Sheng and Fu Rong

Translated by   Lao An, Wang Bo,
Li Yanwen and Zhao Xiufeng

Version revised by An Zengcai

Shandong Friendship Publishing House

First Edition 1996
ISBN 7—80551—768—1/R · 11

Published by
Shandong Friendship Publishing House
Shengli Street, Jinan, China
Printed by
Shandong People's Printing House
Distributed by
China International Book Trading Corporation
35 Chegongzhuang Xilu, Beijing 100044, China
P.O. Box 399, Beijing, China

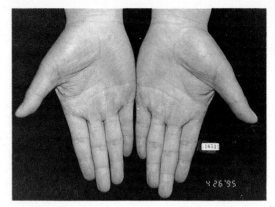

1. name:Wang   sex:female   age:31   marital status:married
case:migraine
①The color of the palm is red mixed with white,while the finger knuckles are bluish purple;
②At the middle and end of Line 2 there is the presence of "大"-shaped lines;and
③The second segment of the index finger is short with the presence of " * "-shaped lines.

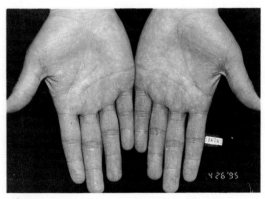

2. name:Jiao   sex:male   age:28   marital status:married
case:coronary heart disease(arrhythmia and angina pectoris)
①The palm is bluish purple mixed with red and is rosy and lustrous;
②There is the presence of " * "-shaped lines between Line 1 and Line 2;and
③The nails on both palms appear as square nails.

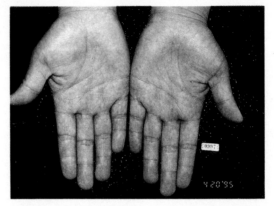

3. name：Tian　sex：female　age：31　marital status：married
case：chronic gastritis

①The palm shows a mixed color of blue，red and yellow，and the area designated as *Zhe* looks obviously pale yellow；

②The area designated as *Zhen* is sagging with" # "-shaped and" ＊ "-shaped lines；and

③In the area designated as *Gen* there is the presence of deep" # "-shaped striped lines.

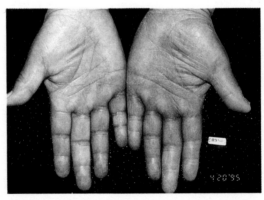

4. name：Fu　sex：female　age：53　marital status：married
case：anemia

①The palm is pale and lusterless；

②Line 2 is extended and untidily arranged" ＋ "-shaped lines are faintly visible；and

③The fingers look cylinder-like.

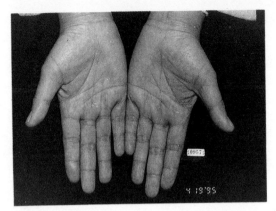

5. name：Wang sex：female age：42 marital status：married
case：cholecystitis and cholelithiasis
①The palm is crimson in color and plump in form；
②There is the presence of" * "-shaped," # "-shaped and" × "-shaped lines in the area designated as *Xun* on both palms；and
③The area designated as *Gen* looks bluish purple in color.

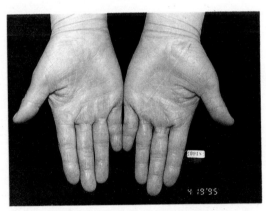

6. name：Ju sex：female age：34 marital status：married
case：constipation
①The palm is rosy mixed with bluish purple；
②There are quite a number of feather-shaped branching or secondary lines on Line 3；and
③The nails are pale and lusterless，and there are some deep and uneven vertical ridges on the thumb.

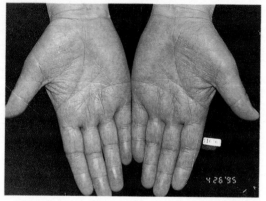

7. name: Zhang   sex: female   age: 53   marital status: married
case: diabetes

①The palm looks scarlet red, which is particularly noticeable at the tips of all the fingers;

②The acid area is obviously larger than the base area; and

③In the area designated as *Qian*, two relatively deep horizontal lines can be seen extending parallelly toward the upper part of the thenar; and the lines in area designated as *Kan* are disordered.

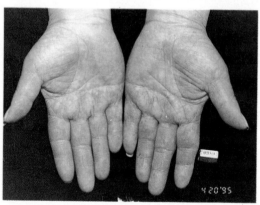

8. name: Gao   sex: female   age: 28   marital status: married
case: neurasthenia

①The palm shows a mixed color of red and white;

②Line 2 is excessively extended and there is the formation of triangular insular lines at its end; and

③In the area designated as *Li* under the middle finger there are disordered lines.

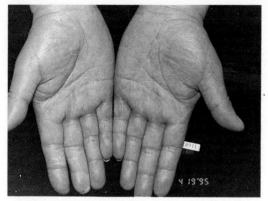

9. name: Kang   sex: female   age: 42   marital status: married
case: hyperplasia of the mammary glands
①The palm shows a mixed color of red and white;
②There is the formation of leaf-shaped insular lines on Line 1 and Line 2; and
③On the section of Line 1 under the ring finger there is the presence of insular lines.

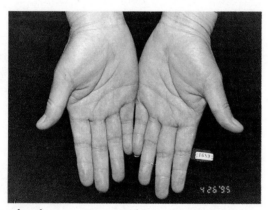

10. name: Li   sex: female   age: 52   marital status: married
case: angina pectoris
①The starting point of Line 2 is too low and is overextended;
②There are "×"-shaped lines between Line 1 and Line 2;
③In the area designated as *Qian* there are "＊"-shaped lines; and
④In the area designated as *Li* there are "＊"-shaped lines, too.

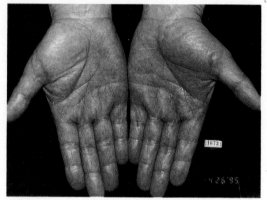

11. name:Chen　sex:male　age:63　marital status:married
case:prostatic hyperplasia
①Line 11 is extended;
②There are insular lines at the end of Line 3;and
③In area designated as *Kun* there are disordered lines.

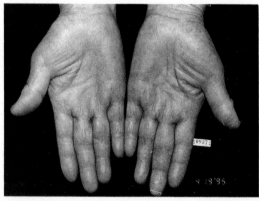

12. name:Li　sex:female　age:56　marital status:married
case:rheumatoid arthritis
①The surface of the palm is glossy;
②The knuckles are stiff and deformed;
③The surface of the palm is coarse;and
④Near Line 2 there are disordered lines.

Contents

Foreword

When it had achieved the great and decisive accomplishment in its evolution as marked by the division of labor between the hand and the foot, the human race, the most advanced biological colony on this planet, began to step on the shadows of diseases in its marching on. It is true that diseases are not the unfortunate occurrences imposed on human beings alone, but it is man alone that is soberly conscious of the presence of diseases and the sufferings they bring with them. Ever since the first day when he began to stand up on his two feet, as it were, has man engaged himself in the prolonged struggle to combat diseases. Up to the present day, myriad volumes of medical literature have built up numerous monuments in memory of man's progress in his self-salvation.

However, there is no denying of the fact that in comparison with man's cognition of nature and his great efforts to make nature benefit his own existence, or in comparison with man's comprehension of the human world and his experience enriched in maintaining social stability and harmony, man's knowledge of himself and his inquiry into the mystic characters of the physiological activities of the human body, it can be asserted without any exaggeration, are still in their childhood. Let us first take traditional Chinese medical science as an example. *The Yellow Emperor's canon of Internal Medicine*[1], produced in ancient China, remains to serve as one of the most important source books for the diagnosis and treatment of diseases for today's professional physicians

1

practicing traditional Chinese medicine. What is more, in the long-term development of human history, man has often vascillated between ignorance and intellegence and confused the dividing line between superstition and science, thus having repeatedly travelled into absurd dead lanes in his struggle to combat diseases. For another example, it was only during the 1930s and the 1940s that scientists from a few developed countries began to take up seriously as their important subjects in their researches the mystic phenomena of the human body by basing themselves upon the most advanced branches of natural sciences including biological engineering.

Since all objects exist in a universal state of correlations, the internal changes and biological activities of the human body will necessarily present many an external feature, the study of which may enable us to realize the internal conditions of the human body. Bian Que[2], for example, the reknowned physician of ancient China, was an expert on medical diagnosis and treatment through observing one's complexion and the color and luster of the skin.

The hand, one of the masterpieces of the Maker, is not only superb and exquisite in its structure and agreeably coordinative in man's work, but also capable of making tools. Besides, it is one of the most sensitive part of the human body. Labor has created man, but first and foremost, it has created man's hand and brain. Do we not have enough reasons to believe that the massive lines on the palm have resulted from the symultaneous evolution with the brain? If it were not so, then, why do all other primates except for the ape have no palmar lines at all? Furthermore, why can the two thick and distinct palmar lines of the ape in no way be compared with those of the human being? Therefore, cannot we further deduce and believe that the complicated formation of the palmar lines of the human being is no other than a kind of mystic information of the mechanisms and pathologic changes of the human body? Findings obtained in the study of man's palmar lines tell us that the innate relationships between the palmar lines and various diseases are beyond any doubt.

Naturally, the identification of palmar lines and diagnosis by observing them are not so easy and simple as imagined. If the external expressions of things were completely identical with their essence, then, all sciences would become unnecessary. The palmar lines and their subtle and delicate changes not only transmit the information of the pathologic changes of the human body, but are contributed to by such factors as hereditary codes, normal biological activities, different personality features, emotional changes and different states of mind caused by the living environments, different modes of thinking, etc., thus bringing forth the complexity and difficulty in the medical study of palmar lines. Only when one is guided with a scientific and dialectical mode of thinking and has come into possession of a great amount of first-hand data accumulated in one's practice for the study and analysis, can one make desirable achievements in this field.

"A small sign can indicate a great trend." The human body is a grand and complicated system, and all its branch systems are correlative and interactive. Once we have obtained a clear knowledge of the relationships between the changes of the palmar lines and the occurrence, development and change of diseases, then, measured with the standards set up by the United Nations Educational, Scientific and Cultural Organization (UNESCO) for advanced modern diagnostics (i. e., painless, woundless, and easy to apply), will the method of diagnosing through observing palmar lines be possible to become the most scientific and advanced method

3

which is economical and easy to apply and popularize.

The medical study of palmar lines is a very young discipline, but it is right because of this that it is full of vitality and has a promised prospect all the more. It might be envisaged that between the palmar lines and diseases there is a mystic passage of which we have not yet known. Someday, hopefully, if we are able not only to diagnose diseases by examing the palmar lines, but also to carry on treatments directly on the palm and remove the pathologic palmar lines so that various diseases can thus be cured, then, what a future of full freedom shall we enjoy!?And, such is the aspiration and pursuit of mine.

Wang Chenxia
July, 1993, in Lanzhou, China

Notes

1. *The Yellow Emperor's Canon of Internal Medicine*, or "Internal Medicine" for short, is the earliest medical classic extant in China. It began to be circulated in the Warring States Period (475--221 BC) and its authorship remains unknown. It consists of two parts: "Plain Questions" and "Miraculous Pivot." The former deals chiefly with basic theories of medicine, while the latter, acupuncture. ······tr.

2. Bian Que was a renowned physician of the 5th century BC, and was the first recorded in Chinese history. It has been widely believed that he was particularly skillful in pulse-feeling and acupuncture and also in treatment of various diseases. According to historical records, during his life-time, he travelled throughout the country and practiced medicine and thus won great fame. His biography and some of his case records are carried in such Chinese classical works as *The Records of the Historian* and *A Collection of Strategies and Policies Proposed for the Warring States*. ·· tr.

Chapter one   Inquiry into the Mystery of
Palmar Lines as a Subject of Ancient Origin

Owing to their historical limitations, the ancients travelled a tortuous path in their study of palmar lines as they made no distinction between witchcraft and the art of healing. And so, they did not hand down any systematic data in this field. However, their efforts did pave the way for the later generations to carry on further studies and thus deserve our memory.

According to *the Yellow Emperor's Canon of Internal Medicine*, the medical book produced as early as more than 2,000 years ago, it was recognized that the parts and the whole of the human body are a dialectical unity and that every part of the body is closely related to the solid viscera and the hollow viscera[1], the channels and the collaterals (*Jing* and *luo* in traditional Chinese medicine)[2], the vital energy and the blood of the body as a whole. Hence, in diagnosing, the conditions of the internal organs can be known through examining the external changes in the five sense organs, the physical features, the complexion and the pulse. In the light of such a theory, the hand naturally reflects the physical conditions of the human body. This belief finds support in the facts that in traditional Chinese medicine there are diagnoses for children through examining their fingerprints and the descriptions about the 25 kinds of *yin* and *yang*[3] symptoms of the human body. There are records of palmistry which began to be practised in China early in the Zhou Dynasty (c. 11th century BC—771 BC), while by the Spring and Autumn Period (770—475 BC) and the Waring States Period (475—221 BC), palmistry had become popular in all the feudal states, being valued and practised everywhere.

In the work *the Yellow Emperor's Canon of Internal Medicine*, there are quite a number of typical discussions about the relationships of the palm with the internal organs and its identification with the internal organs. It is said, for example, "one whose palm center is hot can be identified as being hot in one's hollow viscera, while one whose palm center is cold can be identified as being cold in one's hollow viscera." It is also said in the chapter "Symptoms of Diseases of the Nervous System, the Complxion, the Vital Energy and the Viscera" of the same work, "One who suffers from the disease of the small intestine⋯ shows symptoms of a severe cold all over the body except for the shoulders and the muscle between the little finger and the index finger, all of which are hot." All this purports the relations between the palm and the internal organs. For another example, Bian Que, the famous Chinese physician of the Warring States Period, was an expert on the examination of the changes in the patient's complexion and skin color. Besides, many a determinist studied medical science symultaneously, while numerous well-known physicians were symultaneously well versed in the art of physiognomy. By the time of the Eastern Han Dynasty (317--420) when the system of traditional Chinese medicine had taken shape, man's knowledge about the palm had greatly deepened. In the chapter "Examination of the Bones" in his work *Discourses Weighed in the Balance*, the noted Chinese scholar of the Han Dynasty Wang Chong ex-

pounds, "Never will it fail to diagnose one's disease and pre-
dict one's life or death by examining one's skin lines and examining his bone joints;" "people say that diseases are difficult to be diagnosed, but I believe that is pretty easy. How?
By examining the bones. " As China's renowned exponent of
materialism in the philosophy of the Eastern Han Dynasty,
Wang Chong for the first time in history put forward the
conclusion that "bone joints"and "bones" are related to man'
s "life or death. " This can be regarded as a highly scientific
epitome of the long-term medical practice of the time.

During the last years of the Tang Dynasty (618--907)
and the first years of the Song Dynasty (960--1279), China
gave birth to a Taoist hermit, named Chen Zhuan, who won
great veneration from the following generations. He studied
the theory of mathematics and initiated the "Ziwei Star Al-
gorium"and the "He-Luo Method of Fortune-telling,"which
are still in circulation today. Furthermore, in physiognomy,
he wrote a book named *The Divine Physiognomy of Mayi the
Taoist*, in which there are records of palmar lines of ancients
of remote ages and those of Liu Bang and Xiang Yu of the
Western Han Dynasty. From this we can know that during
the Song Dynasty, people began to collect, analyse and study
palmar lines and gave them different interpretations. Although their assertions contain quite some superstitious and
untrue factors, their records of palmar lines are serious and
accurate and many of them are actually analyses of the physical conditions of the human body. There used to be an old
saying in China that "A physiognomist is unexceptionally a
good doctor. "From such a saying we can deduce that as other diagnoses were developing and prospering, diagnostics by
examining the palm did not develop independently and, in-
stead, remained as a minor means occasionally adopted in
medicine and physiognomy. However, the word

"palmistry" became an accepted term and in wide use. But generally, the art of palmistry (also chiromancy) means at once to diagnose diseases by examining the palm and to foretell one's character, temperament and fate by studying one's palm (true, there are in this respect conjectural and absurd factors, but it is not absolutely so; this point calls for another special treatise). What we are to discuss about here in this book is chiefly its former meaning.

By the time of the Ming Dynasty (1368--1644), diagnoses for children based upon the study of their fingerprints were developed by medical scientists and were practiced widely throughout the country. The works *Details of the Four Methods of Diagnosis*[1], *A Brief Introduction of Diagnosis Based on External Configurations and Complexions* and *the Principles of Diagnosis by Observing the Patient's Complexions* produced during the Qing Dynasty (1644--1911) are, as it were, collections of diagnoses of all the past ages and there are in them quite a number of sections dealing with diagnostics by the palm, which, ever since then, have become an important part of auxiliary clinic diagnostics. In ancient times, the Eight Diagrams[5], the Five Elements[6], the Five Colors[7], the four seasons and the twelve Earthly Branches[8] were all indicated at strictly designated positions across the palm (see Fig. 1).

About 3,000 years ago in ancient India, some Brahmanists hoarded up in a cave three works on palmistry with inscriptions on human hides, in which there are many exquisite patterns in imitation of human palmar lines drawn in human blood. Most probably, they were the original records of palmistry left behind by men through observing, studying and summarising the lines on their own palms.

Palmistry originated in ancient India. During the 4th century BC, with the expedition to India under the command

4

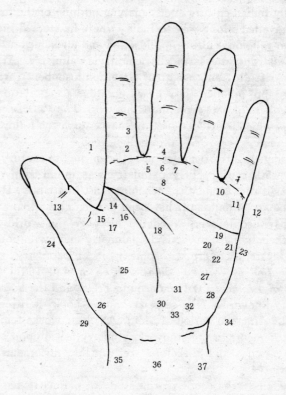

Fig. 1

1. *si*   2. *wood*   3. *Xun*   4. *wu*   5. *red*   6. *Li*   7. *fire*   8. *summer*
9. *wei*   10. *earth*   11. *Kun*   12. *shen*   13. *chen*   14. *wood*   15. *Zhen*
16. *spring*   17. *blue*   18. *Mingt'ang*   19. *white*   20. *autumn*
21. *Dui*   22. *metal*   23. *you*   24. *mao*   25. *earth*   26. *Gen*   27. *metal*
28. *Qian*   29. *yin*   30. *water*   31. *winter*   32. *black*   33. *Kan*
34. *xu*   35. *chou*   36. *zi*   37. *hai*

of Alexander the Great, it was brought back to the West. At the time, the great Greek philosopher Pythagorus was attracted by Indian culture, and, making nothing of the hardships, travelled a long way to India, where he studied India's brilliant religion, culture, philosophy and medicine and developed a strong interest in that country's palmistry. Afterwards, Aristotle, another great Greek philosopher, carried palmistry into practice and, based upon his accumulation of large numbers of data, completed his work *The Palmistry of Aristotle*, which exerted a great influence upon the following generations.

During the historical period between the 5th century BC and the 15th century BC, palmistry was inhibited by the church as it runs against the teachings of Christianity. However, the art of palmistry has been handed down thanks to the Gypsy people who wandered all over the world and earned their living by practising palmistry and divination.

In Japan, there are also some books on palmistry, such as *Divination by Palmar Lines* written around 1681, *The Manual of Plamistry* written around 1789, and the book on palmistry known as "the secretly handed book" written by Hayashi during the Period of Meiji. All these works register the achievements in the study of palmistry based upon practical experience and therefore are valuable documents on palmistry.

In China, the scope of the study of palmistry has not been as large as that of the study of physiognomy, and it is still at a relatively low level. Presently, the palmistry currently popular in the world, having absorbed the essence of the palmistry of ancient China, the palmistry of Europe, the palmistry of Japan, and the palmistry of the Gypsy people and having been incorporated with a great amount of knowledge of modern sciences, has gradually discarded the subjectively conjectural and superstitious coloring and has been endowed with considerable scientific significance. Nowadays on the book market there are quite some books dealing with the relationships of palmistry and physiognomy with diseases. All such books are based, to different extents, upon the summary of people's practical experience and are therefore worth our study.

The 20th century is an age of information. All disciplines are being subdivided more and more elaborately and their studies are more and more specialized. For example, palmistry is now concerned with the study of the relationships between one's personality traits, psychology, physiology, pathology and other aspects and the size, thickness and color of the hand, the length, the crookedness and thickness of the fingers, the finger spaces, the color and configuration of the nails, the distribution and forms of the palmar lines, and so on. I myself have experieced quite some twists and turns in my study of palmar lines and have suffered numerous distresses and hardships. As far as palmar lines are concerned, nobody wears the same as any other does. Indeed, it is a painstaking job to find out diagnostic laws from among such tangled and complicated palmar lines. Because of the lack of a specialized hospital engaged in diagnosing by the palm and reference documents, I used to first diagnose by the palm of the patient and then have my diagnosis confirmed by conventional diagnosis. Thus, I actually followed a line of "synthetical diagnosis."Later, I felt sure of my dignosing by examining palmar lines and began to resort to it solely. Now, after more than 10years' study and experiments with 100,000 cases, I have epitomized some laws which govern the identification of palmar lines with more than 100 diseases.

Notes:

1. They are special terms employed in traditional Chinese medical science. The five solid viscera (the five *zang*-organs) refer to the heart, the liver, the spleen, the lung and the kidney, while the six hollow viscera (the five *fu*-organs) refer to the gallbladder, the stomach, the small intestine, the large intestine, the bladder and the "sanjiao" (i. e. , three portions of the body cavities housing the internal organs and animating their functions). ·· tr.

2. The *jing* and the *luo* (channels and collaterals) refer, in traditional Chinese medical science, to the meridian system of specific conduits for the circulation of blood and *qi* throughout the body. The channels (*jing*) are the main conduits and are deeply situated, while the collaterals (*luo*) are the superfacial network interconnecting the channels as well as all portions of the body. ····························· tr.

3. The *yin* and *yang* theory is an important constuent of the theory of traditional Chinese medical science, and is originated from the combination of ancient philosophical theory and medical practice. ······· tr.

4. The four methods of diagnosis in traditional Chinese medicine include observation of the patient's complexion, expression, movements, tongue, etc. ; auscultation and smelling; interrogation; and pulse feeling and palpation. ·· rt.

5. The Eight Diagrams, originally carried in *the Book of Changes*, are eight groups of trigrams, composed of the "—" and "--" signs. The former stands for the yang, while the latter, for the yin. The first diagram is named *Qian*, symbolized as "☰"; the second named *Kun*, as "☷"; the third *Zhen*, as "☳"; the fourth *Xun*, as "☴"; the fifth Kan, as "☵"; the sixth *Li*, as "☲"; the seventh *Gen*, as "☶"; and the eighth *Dui*, as "☱". In *the Book of Changes*, it is held that the Eight Diagrams essentially symbolize heaven, earth, thunder, wind, water, mountain and river respectively, and most important of all are the *Qian* and *Kun*, which symbolize the primal sources of all natural and social phenomena. ·······tr.

6. The five elements refer to wood, fire, earth, metal and water. Ancient Chinese thinkers used them to signify the origins and diversities of the universe. ··· tr.

7. The five colors refer to blue, red, yellow, white and black. In Chinese tradition, they used to be regarded as pure colors. ······· tr.

8. The twelve Earthly Branches, in traditional Chinese calendar,

are used in combination with the Heavenly Stems to designate years, months, days and hours. Each of the Branches has a name. They are by transliteration *zi*, *chou*, *yin*, *mao*, *chen*, *si*, *wu*, *wei*, *shen*, *you*, *xu*, and *hai*. ·· tr.

Chapter Two   The Hand and the Skin and Lines of the Palm

I . The Dissection of the Hand

The hand is the material basis for diagnosis by observing palmar lines. Only when one is provided with the knowledge about the distribution and formation of the skeleton, muscles, blood vessels, adipose tissues and nerves of the hand, can one adequately understand the features of the lines and colors of the skin of the hand and thus lay the foundation for diagnosis by observing palmar lines.

The frontal end of the upper limb of the human body, the portion from the wrist joint to the finger nails, is named the hand.

The skeleton of the hand is composed of 27 bones. At the bottom of the hand base there are two parallel rows of 8 ossicles known as carpal bones. In front of these carpal bones are 5 metacarpal bones. In front of these metacarpal bones are 14 phalanxes, 2 of which are of the thumb and 12 of which are equally shared by the other four fingers (see Fig. 2).

The muscles of the hand are divided into 3 groups: the lateral muscles, the medial muscles and the intermediate muscles. The lateral muscles are located along the lateral of the thumb and form the prominence in the lateral, known as "large thenar." The medial muscles are located along the lateral of the little finger and form the prominence in its lateral, known as "small thenar." The intermediate muscles are located at the center of the palm. Besides these internal muscles of the hand as mentioned above, there are more than 20

10

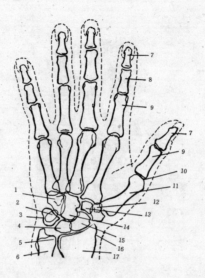

Fig. 2

1. *hamate bone*   2. *pisiform bone*   3. *triangular bone*   4. *lunate bone*
5. *small head of the ulnar*   6. *ulnar*   7. *phalangette*
8. *middle phalanx*   9. *coxal phalanx   phanlangette*   9. *coxal phalanx*
10. *sesamoid cartilage*   11. *metacarpal bone*   12. *trapezium bone*
13. *lesser trapezium bone*   14. *capitate bone*   15. *navicular bone*
16. *styloid process of the radius*   17. *radius*

other muscles which start in the forearm and terminate at
the metacarpal bones or the phalanxes, known as the external muscles of the hand. The number of the muscles of the
hand and their structure are greater and more complicated
than those of the muscles in any portion of the human body.
It is just because of this that the hand can perform meticu-

lous activities (see Fig. 3).

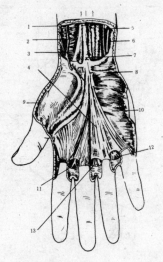

Fig. 3

1. *Linear flexor muscle of the finger*
2. *radial flexor muscle of the wrist*
3. *radial artery*   4. *palmar aponeurosis*   5. *ulnar artery*   6. *ulnar nerve*
7. *tendon palmaris longus*   8. *transverse carpal ligament*
9. *superfacial branch of the radial nerve*   10. *short palmar muscle*
11. *common palmar digital arteries*   12. *web-space*
13. *proper palmar digital nerves*

The blood circulating in the hand is particularly abundant. The main blood vessels which enable the blood circulation throughout the hand are the radial artery, the ulnar artery, the radial vein and the ulnar vein. When the radial artery and the ulnar artery have reached the palm, they are divided respectively into the superfacial and deep branches, each of which is divided again into numerous delicate and thin sub-branches, running throughout all the palm and fingers. The endings of the arteries are joined with the endings of the veins so that the venous blood flows back to the venous system through the radial vein and the ulnar vein, thus maintaining the regular circulation of the blood through the hand (see Fig. 4). As the blood capillaries of the hand are extremely abundant and the blood circulation is very active, many physiological and pathological phenomena all over the human body can be identified on the hand.

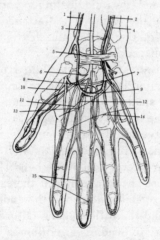

Fig. 4

1. *radial artery*   2. *ulnar artery*   3. *median nerve*   4. *ulnar nerve*
5. *horizontal ligament of the wrist*
6. *recurrent branch of the median nerve*
7. *deep branch of the ulnar nerve*
8. *deep palmar arch*   9. *superfacial palmar arch*
10. *main artery of the thumb*   11. *thenar lines*
12. *arteriae metacarpal*   13. *palmar lines*
14. *remote palmar lines*   15. *proper palmar digital nerve*

The main nerves of the hand are the median nerve, the ulnar nerve and the radial nerve. As it serves as the chief motoral nerve for the frontal muscles of the forearm and the large thenar muscles, the median nerve is concerned with the chief function of motion of the hand, and it is also the main sensory nerve for the surface of the palm. Injury of the median nerve leads to such motional obstacles as failure in turning forward the forearm, failure in turning the wrist and weakness in spreading it out, failure in crooking the thumb, the index finger and the middle finger and failure of the thumb in touching the palm. The flattened palm resulting from the atrophy of the thenar muscles is known as "ape hand" or "claw-shaped hand."

When it reaches the wrist, the ulnar nerve enters the palm along the outer lateral of the orbicular bone of the wrist through the shallow surface of the horizontal ligament of the wrist and the tendon membrance of the palm. It is the chief motional nerve for the hand muscles and the musculi flexor carpi ulnaris of the forearm as well as the sensory nerve for the ulnar lateral skin of the hand. Injury of the ulnar nerve will cause the weakening of the capability to turn the wrist, the incapability to crook the ending segments of the index finger and the little finger, failure in bending the thumb, incapability to bend inward or spread out the fingers and loss of sense for the smaller thenar muscles and the little finger. A flattened palm caused by the atrophy of the smaller thenar muscles is known as "claw-shaped hand."

The deep branches of the radial nerve derive many sub-branches, which control the rear muscles of the forearm and the skin on the back of the forearm, while the superficial branches of the radial nerve are dispersed in the radial lateral of the back of the hand and in the skin along the radial lateral of the back of the two fingers. Injury of the radial

14

nerve will show failure in turning the wrist and stretching the fingers, resulting in a "drooping wrist," incapability to spread out the thumb and loss of sense for the skin within the area between the thumb and the index finger.

II. Features of the Skin on the Palm

Modern scientific researches on the human body manifest that besides its irresplaceable function as part of the external human body, the hand, as far as man's tactual sensation is concerned, plays a greater role than any skin area in other parts of the body. It serves not only as a tool to safeguard the living human body, but also as a guide for man to perceive the unknown world. When one has lost one's eyesight, man's most important sensory faculty, the ear and the hand will be the first to remedy the defect caused for the living body by the loss of the eyesight. The status the hand holds among all the organs of the human body and the wide range of its functions prove that it has extremely close relationships with the internal organs. Hence, to study such relationships, one has to be furnished with a scientific knowledge about the palm and the skin on the palm.

The skin occupies the largest surface area of the human body as it covers the skeleton, the muscles, the circulatory system and the internal organs. Covered all over with cleavage lines and dotted with pores of sweat glands, it performs the functions of protecting the body, helping the breathing and excreting and regulating the temperature of the body.

Besides the general functions of the skin, the palmar skin has its own features. Its particularity and individuality make it the most preferable skin area for observation.

1. With Sweat Glands but Without Fine Hairs

That the palmar skin has sweat glands but does not have fine hairs is one of the most important features of the palm. The lines on the base of the palm can best and fully reveal their own development as they are free of the interference of the pores and fine hairs in the skin, whereas the lines on the skin of the back of the hand, due to the large numbers of the pores of the sweat glands, form a checkered network on the skin, and, in addition, there are the fine hairs, thus making it more difficult to directly observe the cleavage lines on the skin. Furthermore, the temperature of the back of the hand is similar to that of the surface of the body, while the temperature of the palm base is about 0. 2--0. 8℃ higher than that of the surface of the body. As it were, it is the measurement for the secretion of the sweat glands of the palmar lateral, which is concerned with one's moods. This also proves the corretationship between the palm and the internal physiological mechanisms.

2. Massive and Active Subcutaneous Circulation and Microcirculation of Blood

The massive and active subcutaneous circulation and microcirculation of blood in the hand enable a great amount of bioelectric information and non-bioelectric information to gather in the palm.

Due to the difference between the blood supply and the regulation of the microcirculation of blood, the area controlled by the very small blood vessels and the microcirculation of blood tends to change in its form. In other words, the catabolism of the cell is affected, which gives rise to bulges or sags, growing or whithering to the outer form of the cell, thus forming dithches and ridges shown as new cleavages on the skin. For instance, when the blood in the endings contains too much fat, the surplus grains of the fat will be delivered to and gather in the palm and form mounts. This shows that there is too much fat contained in the blood , and can be identified as lipoidemia. Meanwhile, such changes will soon send out information and find their expressions in the palmar lines.

3. The Concentration Area of Nerve Endings

The ancients used to say, "The ten fingers are connected with the heart. " Dissection shows that the nerves of the fingers are directly connected with the cerebrum, which means that the hand has a close relationship with the brain and the heart. The sensitivity of the palmar skin is much higher than that of any other skin, while the tactile sensation of the hand is keener than that of any part of the body. Every member of the human kind uses the hand as a tool, which is more sensitive to cold or heat, softness or hardness, dryness or wetness and unsmoothness and smoothness than any other portion of the human body. The massiveness and activities of the nerve endings also play an important role in the generation and mutability of the palmar lines.

4. A Concentration Area of the Jing and Luo and the Acupuncture Points[1]

There are altogether 6 *jing* and *luo* which channel the hand, of which the heart *jing*, the small intestine *jing*, the pericardium *jing* and the *sanjio*[2] *jing* all terminate in the heart. Henece, the middle finger, the index finger and the little finger are all closely related with the heart. According to the book *Magic Therapies of Acupuncture Points on the Hand* published in Chinese by Sichuan Science and Technology Press, China, there are altogether 75 acupuncture points all over in the hand. Mr Gakuta Haratomi of Japan, who has practiced physical massage for years, has discovered that there are 47 reflex areas in the hand (see Fig. 5, Fig. 6, Fig. 7 and Fig. 8).

Large numbers of tests with and researches on the

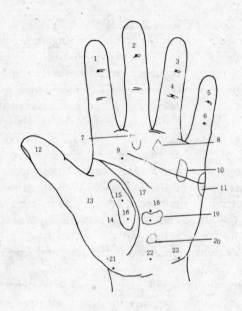

Fig. 5

1. *large intestine*　2. *acupoint for the heart*　3. *acupoint for the lung*
4. *acupoint for the liver*　5. *acupoint for the kidney*　6. *Mingmen*
7. *area for the ear and pharynx*　8. *area for the palm*
9. *point for cough and asthma*　10. *area for heart beating*
11. *area for the genital organs*　12. *Shaoshang*　13. *thoracic cavity*
14. *area for respiration*　15. *stomach*　16. *spleen*
17. *center of the palm*
18. *point for sweating*　19. *area for the stomach and intestine*
20. *area for the leg and foot*　21. *Taiyuan*　22. *Taling*　23. *Shenmen*

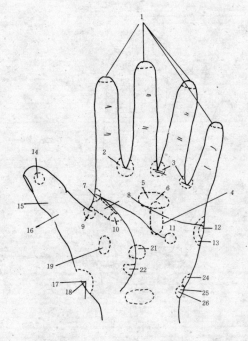

Fig. 6

1. *portion of the head*   2. *eye*   3. *ear*   4. *adenal gland*
5. *thymus gland*   6. *lung*   7. *stomach*   8. *colon*
9. *portion of the neck*   10. *intestine*   11. *pancreas*   12. *shoulder*
13. *pancreas*   14. *hypophysis*   15. *portion of the head*
16. *nerve system*   17. *womb*   18. *penis*   19. *prostate*   20. *thyroid*
21. *bladder*   22. *pile*   23. *lumbosacral portion*   24. *knee*
25. *testis*   26. *overy*

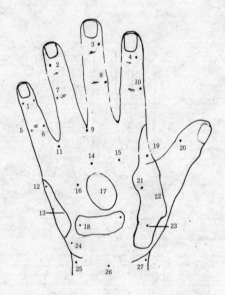

Fig. 7

1. *Shaoch'ung*   2. *Kuanch'ung*   3. *Chungch'ung*   4. *Shangyang*
5. *point for the rear of the head*   6. *Huiyin*
7. *point for the lateral of the head*
8. *point for the top of the head*   9. *point for the faux*
10. *point for the front of the head*   11. *Yemen*   12. *Houhsi*
13. *reflexion area of the spinal cord*
14. *area for the neck-pharynx*   15. *point for the top of the neck*
16. *Chungtu*   17. *area for thoracico-abdominal portion*
18. *area for spine-wiaist-leg*   19. *Sanchian*
20. *point for the eye*   21. *Hoku*
22. *reflexion area for blood pressure*
23. *area for the pain in the nose*   24. *carpal bone*
25. *Yangku*   26. *Yangch'ih*   27. *Yanghsi*

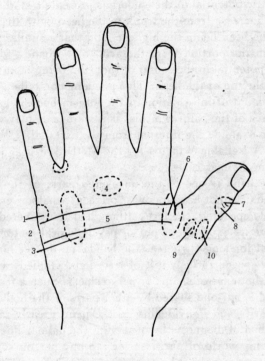

Fig. 8

1. *shoulder*   2. *scapular region*   3. *area for bones*   4. *thorax*
5. *diaphram*   6. *area for the pharynx-thorax*   7. *upper palate*
8. *lower palate*   9. *tonsil*   10. *area for the lymph*

acupuncture points on the hand reveal that the hand bears similar bioelectric characteristics to those of the head, that the electric potential of the epidermis presents a state of progressive increase from the trunk to the head, with that in the top of the head being the highest, and that a similar state is shown in the portion from the arm to the hand, with the electric potential in the center of the palm being next highest only to the top of the head. This phenomenon tells us that a great amount of information of the human body is gathered in the area of the palm, whichis, as it were, a display window for us to examine the internal from the external.

5. A Reliable Window for the Method of Diagnosis by Observing Palmar Lines

The hand is one of the uncovered parts of the human body and does not have its own "privacy" whatsoever. Comparatively speaking, the face, although also uncovered, tends to change its expressions out of psychological factors when looked at for long, whereas the hand, no matter how long and how concentratively it is observed and studied, will never have the sense of shame or nervousness. Such a feature of the hand is not one shared by other parts of the body. Such particularity and individuality of the palm greatly facilitate the method of diagnosis by observing the palmar lines.

In this world of ours, never can any person share the same patterned palmar lines with any other; they are unique. Hence, the specific and unique palmar lines of one display the features of the given living body, and they can never be imitated or reproduced on the palm of any other person. This allows that the diagnosis through observing the palmar lines of the given person is responsible to the particular given living body, thus guaranteeing its reliability. All the above-mentioned advantages of the palm make it the specially designated part of the body for the observation of the cleavage lines for medical purposes.

Ⅲ. A Preliminary Inquiry into the Contributing Factors to the Palmar Lines

So far there have not been systematic data relating with the study of the palmar lines, and the discussions about them in the method of diagnosis by observation applied in traditional Chinese medicine and in dermoglyphics of Western medicine are rare and fragmentary. However, the rapid progress in biological science has enlarged our vision in the renewed study of the organic relationships between the palmar lines and the living body.

It has been discovered so far that palmar lines exist only on the palms of the viviparous primates as well as human beings. But compared with the palmar lines of other primates, those of the human beings are more massive and varied. This indicates that such a phenomenon cannot be explained with the external environmental effects only, and that it calls for a further study of the innate correlationship between the formation of the palmar lines and the organic body.

Firstly, palmar lines are hereditary, including normal heredity and pathological heredity.

1. The Normal Heredity of the Palmar Lines

Normal palmar lines comprise three main lines and the derivative lines from them. The length, the radian and the branching form of the main lines bear a similarity or even a complete sameness on the palms of persons of close consanguinity. The 14 lines referred to in this work also reveal a tendency toward family heredity. Such heredity may be direct or indirect, and similar palmar lines are often found on the palms of several persons of the same generation.

2. The Pathological Heredity of the Palmar Lines

Pathological palmar lines as tokens of some diseases can be present symultaneously on the palms of several persons of close consanguinity. Such pathologicasl lines may be either of recessive heredity or of dominant heredity. For instance, diabetes is a hereditary disease and its pathological lines may be found symultaneously on the palms of persons belonging to different generations of the diabelic's family. However, everyone who wears such palmar lines is not necessarily a diabelic. Once the condition appropriate for diabetes is provided by external factors (such as environments, diet, etc.), such a hereditary disease will take place, though such conditions are not necessarily the pathogeny of the disease for other persons. Therefore, it testifies that diagnosis by observing palmar lines does have the forecasting function for some diseases (special discussions of the point will be dedicatcd in the following chapters).

In the study of both recessive heredity and dominant heredity, atavism of the palmar lines has been discovered, as extremely resembling pathological lines in token of cholecystitis and oncoma on the palms of grand parents and grand children.

Secondly, the embryonic development is one of the contributing factors to the formation of the palmar lines. Researches show that the cleavage lines begin to develop in the 13th week of the embryonic development and take shape in about the 19th week. As a matter of fact, the dermal papilla protrudes toward the epiderm and forms many a relatively neat mammillary line (alternately known as "ridges"), and between the ridges many sagging ditches are formed, and the ridges and ditches thus form the fingerprints and the palmar lines. The fingerprint falls into a fixed pattern when one is born and remains unchanged for life long, while the palmar lines are in a constant change in their depth and growth along with one's age, life experiences, living environments, dietetic habit and pathological conditions, etc. (see Fig. 9).

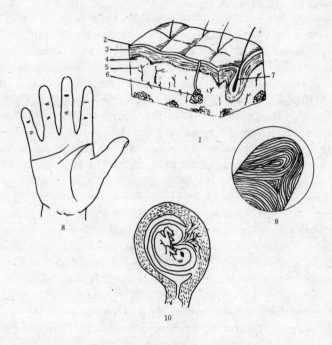

Fig. 9

1. *structure of the skin*   2. *cleavage lines*   3. *epiderm*
4. *papilla of the true skin*   5. *capillary*   6. *sweat gland*
7. *papilla of hair*   8. *folding line*   9. *fingerprints*
10. *foetus during the period between the 13th week and the 19th week*

Besides the above-mentioned contributing factors, the formation of the lines is also concerned with the nutrition assimilated by the foetus in the womb, the posture in which the foetus grasps its hand and the pressure thus produced.

Thirdly, the formation of the delicate and small lines of the palm is closely concerned with the postnatal living conditions, the activity of the palm and the occurrence of diseases. One who often holds a pen in his hand is usually muscular and thus both his large and small thenars are bulging, which causes Line 1 and Line 3 to be deep and long and Line 2 to be relatively short and flat. Many a disease may cause the palmar lines from their non-existence to existence or from their existence to non-existence. One who has never suffered from appendicitis does not wear any abnormal lines in the corresponding area of his palm, while one who suffers from appendicitis bears " * "-shaped or " # "-shaped lines in the corresponding area of his palm. After the surgical operation of appendectomy, however, stellate lines may appear in that area, but in a few years after receiving the operation, all these lines will disappear completely provided that he does not suffer from any sequels such as intestinal conglutination. If diseases such as conglutination do occur, these lines will be disordered and turn into " * " -shaped and stellate lines or lines encircled by a "☐" -shaped frame.

Living in this natural world, man is in a constant exchange of tangible and intangible substances with the universe, the most direct modes of which are breathing and eating. All such exchanges may possibly leave their traces on the palm. An improper diet, which causes gastro-intestinal diseases, may lead to the irregulation of the metabolism of fat in the body. In such a case, excessive bulges or sags will appear in the corresponding area of the palm, thus causing the disordering of the lines. The irregulation of the respiratory function, which breaks the equilibrium of the acid and the base in the body, will result in the changes in the proportional surface of the acid-base areas on the palm. The imbalance of the trace elements in the body can also find its expression in the hand. For example, acalcecosis may make the index finger grow for an excessive length. All these testify that the changes in the palmar lines are concerned with the exchnages of substances between the human body and the universe, and that improper changes may lead to the disorder of the internal environments of the human body, which may leave traces on the hand.

Informatics is regarded as one of the three great mainstays for modern science and technology, and its development and progress will exert a far-reaching influence on and give a great impetus to modern science and technology. Information is the objective realistic variable state of the motion of matters, while energy is the dynamic power for the motion of matters. Then, what kind of states which indicate the motion of matters can we find in the human body? And what kind of modes do the changes of information assume?

In terms of informatics, the human body is a perfect, highest level self-controlled system. All its component parts are connected and interacted. Under normal conditions, it is automatically regulated and balanced by a number of regulatory systems, so that the normal physical activities and the function of identifying and handling information of the human body are maintained. However, when troubles or pathologic changes occur in some of the regulatory systems, the human body will necessarily send out information in their corresponding portions. Relatively speaking, the palm is the portion where various information of the human body is amassed, and therefore various normal and abnormal information can be identified on the palm.

There is a great variety of the information sent out by the human body, but, basically, there are two categories: the bioelectric information and the non-bioelectric information. The former includes the cardioelectric wave, the brain wave, the myoelectric wave, the neuropotential, the retinalpotential, the body surface potential, the cold light, the bioelectric action of individual cells, the electric wave sent out by the human body, etc. The latter includes the blood pressure, the pulse, the heart sounds, the body temperature, the respiration, the cleavage lines, the volume and velocity of the blood flow, the volume of gas content in the blood, the color of the epiderm, and the form, the symmetry and distribution of the five sense organs, the four limbs, the trunk and the hairs of the human being. All such information reflects the states of the biologic activities of the human body. The regular changes of such information are concerned with the physiological and pathological states of the human body, and , at the same time, they can find their respective expressions on the palm. Tested with a galvanometer on the palm, the three main palmar lines, i. e., Line 1, Line 2 and Line 3, show a difference in the current volume of the bioelectric information of the body from that of the other areas of the hand. When tested with a galvanometer, the pathologic lines in different areas of the hand emit very different buzzing sounds. This indicates that different diseases send out different information to the hand. Non-bioelectric information, in particular, can be most easily recognized on the palmar lines. For example, such diseases as hypertension, hypotension and arrhythmia show notable signs on the palmar lines, while both fracture and concussion of the brain will leave eternal marks on the lines. It can be stated, therefore; that palmar lines are the records of information transmitted within the body.

Man's hands serve not only as organs for laboring, but also as useful tools to express his sentiments and feelings. Among all the living beings on this planet, only man and the ape wear fingerprints and palmar lines, while all other mammals have only bald palms, being free of any lines. Does this confirm that developed intelligence and enriched feelings have something to do with the palmar lines? Traditional Chinese medical science holds that the human body is an organic entirety, that pathologic changes in the internal organs may find expressions in the tissues of the body surface, and that external phemomena can, within a certain range, reflect the internal conditions. It is recognized that the external features of the physique are contributed to with obvious hereditary factors, but as far as the intellectual state is concerned, it is not certain that hereditary factors play a decisive role, as postnatal education exerts a considerable influence upon one's intelligence. However, the intellectual state during the initial period, just like one's physique, is contributed to by hereditary factors, which may also find expressions on the palm. For instance, those who are feeble-minded, have overworked their brains or suffer from neurosism may show, by different degrees, different palmar lines, resulting from their different dispositions which may either be sanguine or depressive. One's temperament, personality traits and abnormal psychological activities all can give rise to particular lines on the palm and show particular colors on the nails and skin.

To summarize, the formation of palmar lines are concerned with the relationships between the hand and the brain and their exchanges of information with the external world. The brain has its instructions fulfilled with the aid of the hand, while, in return, the hand constantly sends feedbacks of information to the brain. Therefore, their long-term interaction will necessarily leave traces about the thinking processes on the hand.

Notes:

1. acupuncture point (or acupoint): a special term employed in traditional Chinese acupuncture. Acupoints are supposed to be small pulls of the circulating *qi* and blood of channels and viscera where acupuncture or moxibustion is applied. Those points which are situated on the channels (*jing*) are known as "channel (or jing) -points," more than 360 of which are thus located on the 14 regular channels, while those which are not situated on the channels are known as "extra-channel points." ·· tr.

2. *sanjiao*, or tri-*jiao*, in traditional Chinese medical science, is one of the six *fu*-organs including the upper-, middle- and lower *jiao*. The upper one houses the heart and lung; the middle one, the spleen and stomach; and the lower one, the liver , kidney, urinary bladder, small and large intestines. Their function represents the summation of those of the solid and hollow organs. They are also the passageways of *qi* and fluids. ··· tr.

Chapter Three   The Forms of the Five Fingers and the Division of the Areas on the Palm

Ⅰ. The Forms of the Fingers and Their Significance for Diagnosis by Observing the Palmar Lines

The fingers and the palm are the remote endings of the human body and are one of the starting points for the reflux of the blood. Since very ancient times, it has been believed in traditional Chinese medical science that the five fingers reflect the exuberance or feebleness of the five solid vescera and the six hollow vescera. The functions of the body organs interact upon one another and so the change in one organ often affects the whole body, resulting in the malnutrition or dysfunction of all the organs. Following is an introduction of the meanings as shown by the forms of the respective fingers and their significance for the health of the body.

1. The Thumb

The thumb has to do with the hereditary constitution. Generally, one who has a long and robust thumb is healthier, while one who has a thumb which looks excessively thin and weak and even crooked tends to suffer from neurosism, headache or insomnia. One who has too many disordered lines on the first and second segments and has indistinct and disordered lines on the knuckles tends to suffer diseases in the head. Besides, one who has relatively short segments of the thumb which are excessively stiff and difficult to bend generally tends to develop such diseases as apoplexy, headache and heart trouble.

2. The Index Finger

The index finger can be employed to judge the soundness of the function of the liver. Generally, a handsomely round and robust index finger is best. If one has an index finger which looks straight and can be put perfectly together with the middle finger with the first segment being the longest and the other two being slightly shorter progressively, then, this indicates that the person's liver function is sound enough and he himself is free of any diseases. If one has a pale and thin index finger, it is certain that his liver function is not proper, and he himself tends to feel tired in work and be listless in daily life. If the index finger looks flat and crooked with disordered lines and crevices between the fingers, this often signifies the liver function is bad and, at the same time, suggests that the digestive system is not sound enough. If the three segments of the index finger do not share the same length and especially the middle segment has an excessive length, that has something to do with imbalanced assimilation of calcium. Those who have such index fingers mostly tend to receive damnifications in their bones or teeth at an early age.

3. The Middle Finger

The robustness of the middle finger has to do with the health conditions of the heart and the circulatory system. Generally, a round, long and robust middle finger with soft but not feeble knuckles is better, while one which is excessively stiff and hard and lacks elasticity is not so good. Those who have a middle finger which looks straight and not flat and crooked mostly enjoy a fine function of the heart, exuberant vital energy and are energetic and free of any diseases. One whose middle finger looks pale, thin and weak has a bad function of the heart and a bad function of the blood forming mechanism.

One whose middle finger looks flat and crooked with crevices between the fingers, besides an unsound circulatory system, may also have a poor function of the intestinal canals. One who has a middle finger of which the three segments do not share the same length with the middle segment being excessively long tends to develop diseases in his bones and teeth, which signifies that he has a poor function of calcium metabolism.

4. The Ring Finger

The robustness of the ring finger has a close connection with the health condition of the body as a whole. A best ring finger should look round, handsome and robust. One who has a too short ring finger indicates that he is too weak in the vital energy and is often listless. Those whose ring fingers look straight without any crooks and whose knucle lines are round, smooth and strong and are distinct and clear mostly enjoy a sound function of the kidney and the genitals, while those whose ring fingers look pale, thin and weak mostly have a poor function of the kidney and the genitals.

The first segment of the ring finger represents the soundness of the sexual function. One whose first segment of the ring finger is excessively thick and strong tends to suffer from endocrine dysfunction, while one who has an excessively thin and weak first segment tends to be poor in the genital system. The knuckle lines of the first segment of the ring finger signify the same meaning, i. e. , their disorder indicates a poor health, while their completeness and distinction indicate a good health.

The second segment of the ring finger represents the robustness or weakness of one's muscles and bones. Since very ancient times, the skeleton has been in traditional Chinese medical science designated as "water" in nature among the so-called Five Elements. That is, it has a very close relationship with the genital system. Those who have disordered knuckle lines in the second segment are mostly poor in their physical performance and have thin and weak muscles and bones. When lines appear on the edges of the second segment, known as "disease contracting lines," it indicates that the person has a poor health right now. Such lines may increase or decrease along with the worsening or improving of the health.

One whose second segment of the ring finger is excessively long tends to be poor in his assimilation function of calcium, which results in the fragility of the bones and teeth. If it is excessively pale, thin and weak, the same case will occur. One whose ring finger is flat and crooked with crevices between the fingers when put together, besides having a poor urinary system, often has a poor function of the brain, and, at the same time, tends to show such symptoms as of neurosism, headache, and insomnia.

Those who have excessively long ring fingers (i. c., their length surpasses half of the third segment of the middle finger, or, they are nearly on the same level with the middle finger) mostly have a congenital strong constitution by heredity but are apt to suffer postnatal poor health resulting from habits of irregulated life such as drinking, late stay-up and overwork, etc.

5. The Little Finger

The little finger is supposed to reflex the soundness of the digestive system. Generally, a nice little finger should be long, thin and straight without being flat and crooked, and its segments share a symmetrical length. Such appearances of the little finger show that the function of the digestive system is sound enough and its possessor enjoys a good health. Furthermore, such a physique may be handed down to one's children.

One who has a thin, small and weak little finger is subject to intestinal diseases, which may cause indigestion or irregular bowel movement. One whose little finger is flat and crooked with crevices between the fingers when put together is also apt to suffer from intestinal diseases which lead to indigestion. The disordering of the knuckle lines of the little finger,besides indicating the poor physic function of the possessor himself, tends to be handed down to one of his or her children.

II. The Division of Areas across the Palm

The ancients once made profound studies of the health conditions reflected and indicated by palmar lines in different areas designated in accordance with the Eight Diagrams as well as the functions and colors of the palmar lines. The designation of the areas in accordance with the Eight Diagrams (see Fig. 10) offers us most valuable original data to carry on further studies in this field. The following table on pages 37 to 42 is an epitome of the reflections on the palm and the homolgous relations of the organs of the human body.

III. The Homologous Relationships between the Palmar Areas and the Internal Organs

There is a similarity in the cognition of the homologous relationships between the palmar areas and the internal organs shared by the medical studies carried out both in China and in other countries in acient times. For example, the area for the gal lbladder was designated as *"Xun"* in accordance with the Eight Diagrams and "yang water" among the Five Elements by ancient Chinese,while in the Western world the same area has been known as "the Mount of Jupiter," and both versions hold that the area represents the functions of

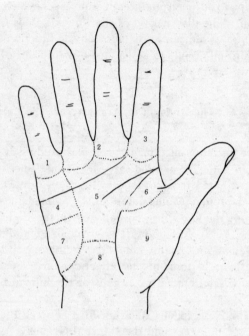

Fig. 10

1. Kun 2. Li 3. Xun 4. Dui 5. Mingt′ang
6. Zhen 7. Qian 8. Kan 9. Gen

designated area	position on the palm	of the five elements	function represented	feature	color	health condition indicated
area designated as *Li*	under middle and ring fingers	fire (of the *yang*)	heart, circulatory system and eyesight	prominent, free of disordered lines	pink	sound heart function, exuberant vital energy, fine eyesight
				red with white spots		cardiac dysfunction, betokening cardiac infarction
				excessive prominence		hyperlipemia
area designated as *Kun*	upper the little finger	earth (the *yin*)	organs in the lower abdomen	prominent	rosy	strong abdominal muscles, normal function of the digestive and genital systems
				disordered lines	dark	looseness of the abdominal muscles, poor function of the large and small intestines
				sagging; distinct contours of blood vessels and bones	pale without color of blood	weakened function of the genital system; for women, sterility with womb cold and a tendency toward creeping chill

designated area	position on the palm	of the five elements	function represented	feature	color	health condition indicated
area designated as Zhen	upper half of the large thenar region encircled by Line 3	wood (the yin)	(of the nervous system	prominent high	moist and red	healthy, normal both of the nerves and the psyche
				muscles stiff or thin, the area encircled by Line 3 very small	pale and lusterless	susceptible to dysfunction of the genital and urinary mechanisms
				disordered untidy lines; hair-shaped crossed stellate lines		nervousness; irregulated life; suscep to neurosis
area designated Xun	under the index finger	wood (the yang)	(of hepaticbiliary system	prominent high	pink	fine function of the liver and the bile
				disordered lines and coarse skin	lusterless	dysfunction of the liver

designated area	position on the palm	of the five elements	function represented	feature	color	health condition indicated
area designated as *Gen*	lower half of the thumb globus, under the area encircled by Line 3	earth (the *yang*)	of spleen and stomach	prominent; muscles soft and lustrous		good appetite; fine function of digestion
				disordered lines and coarse skin	dark hues oval forms	dysfunction of stomach and spleen; stomach trouble
				distinct contours of blood vessels; obvious sagging; muscles thin and few		mostly a poor function of stomach

designated area	position on the palm	of the five elements	function represented	feature	color	health condition indicated
area designated as *Kan*	under the center of the palm	water (of the *yin*)	urinary and genital systems	prominent with soft muscles	lustrous	fine function of both urinary and genital systems
				disordered lines and coarse skin	dark color	malnutrition in childhood; weak of health in adulthood; poor vital energy, and susceptible to fatigue
				blue and distinct contours of blood vessels; sagging; muscles thin and few		dysfunction of the kidney
				loose and incomplete lines on the neck of the hand		dysfunction of the kidney; susceptible to sterility when severe

designated area	position on the palm	of the five elements	function represented	feature	color	health condition indicated
area designated as *Dui*	near the Palmar lateral between the horizontal curving line under the little finger and Line 2	metal (the *yin*)	respiratory system and the large intestine	prominent	lustrously red	good health; exuberant vital energy; sound function of the respiratory system and the large intestine
				loose and disordered lines and coarse skin	dark	feeble in the respiratory system; the lung hurt by intense heat
				sagging; distinct contours of blood vessels	dried pale	infection of the respiratory system; pulmonary emphysema

designated area	position on the palm	of the five elements	function represented	feature	color	health condition indicated
area designated as Qian	under the area designated as Dui above the line of the hand neck	metal (of the yang)	psychologic state and the respiratory system	prominent	fresh color	in sound psyche and exuberant vital energy
				loose and disordered lines; coarse akin	dark	stasis of sentiments and feelings; neurosis
				sagging; distinct contours of bones and blood vessels	dried pale	feeble in the respiratory system; health affected

Above is a table which illustrates the identifications of the areas designated on the palm with the functions of the body widely employed in ancient China.

the liver and the gallbladder. However, I personally believe that it represents cystic diseases, liver troubles, metabolic disorder of fat and the decline of digestive function. The area designated as *Xun* was believed by ancient Chinese to belong to "water" in its nature and to express the rise and fall of the vital energy of the genital organs and the kidney. In Western palmistry, it is believed to represent the functions of the internal secretion, the urinary system and the genital system as well as such symptoms as of sterility and easy fatigue. But I personally believe that this area has a close relationship with uterine diseases and, at the same time, may also reflex the health conditions of middle-aged and old people.

Based upon the summary of my clinic experience for years, I believe that the corresponding points in the palmar areas to the internal organs are not fixed and unitary. Practice has shown that the condition of one given internal organ may be expressed at several reflexing points, and at some points it may express itself in the cleavage lines while at other points it may express itself in the color of the palm.

Why may one organ be able to offer features in several areas for observation? In accordance with the analysis of informatic theory, in the human body, only the spermatic cells and the egg cells are holographic elementary cells, and all the other cells carry only part of the information of the body. This phenomenon of only approximation but not the equivalent to the entirety, I, personally, venture to call it "incomplete information." Since the information is incomplete, we have to seek information from all sides in diagnosing and gather together all incomplete information from different areas so that a relatively "complete" information capacity may be obtained to provide a sound basis for definite diagnoses and avoid distortion and erroneous diagnoses. Especially with cases of malignant tumors, such a synthetic method of observation has a particular clinic significance (see Fig. 11).

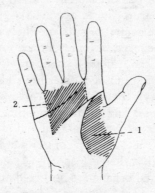

Fig. 11

Personally, I believe that one internal organ presents itself in more than one areas for observation. For instance, the heart, in my opinion, presents itself in three areas, which indicate respectively cor pulmonale, hereditary heart diseases or pathologic organic changes of the heart itself. This is significant for the determination of the pathogenic factors and thus suits the remedy to the case.

The positions and correlations of different organs within the body are also organically represented on the palm. The adjacency of the liver and gall and the interdependence of the heart and the lungs, for example, can be proved by the facts that beside the palmar area representing the liver there is always a reflecting point of the gall, while the three reflexing points of the heart and the lungs are all adjacent or overlapped.

In the division of the palmar areas, general directions

must be determined first. Generally, the tips of the fingers are regarded as "upper," the part close to the wrist as "lower," the starting points of the palmar lines as "upper" and their terninations as "lower;" the side where is the thumb is regared as the "left" and the side where is the little finger as the "right." Thus, such an orientation as "upper," "lower," "left" and "right" can, by and large, determine the location of the focus in the body. Next, the areas of acid and base should also be differentiated and identified in order to obtain a general judgement of the main disease of the patient. The area surrounded by Line 3 is usually regarded as the acid area, which, if large and plump, shows that the constitution tends to be of acid. The area starting from the gap between the index finger and the middle finger and that between the ring finger and the little finger vertically down to Line 2 on the palm is regarded as the base area. The larger this area is, more of base the constitution is; but if it is narrow and small, it is shown that the constitution tends to be of acid. In terms of the susceptibility to diseases, the acid and base constitutions have their respective particularities. Those with an acid constitution are susceptible to such diseases as hypertension, arteriosclerosis, cerebral hemorrhage and diabetes, while those with a base constituion are susceptible to such diseases as hypotension, asthma, gastroptosia and cancer. In diagnosing, observations should be first conducted to find out whether the skin color is not pink and smooth, whether there are not distinct blue contours of the blood vessels, whether the muscles are not plump or sagging and whether there is not the presence of abnormal lines. Generally speaking, the presence of " + " -shaped lines and trangled lines shows slight cases, while the presence of " # " -shaped lines or " * " -shaped lines shows severe cases. Besides, if there is the presence of ringlike or square lines, it shows usually a prolonged case or a scar or a mark left behind by the removal of the corresponding internal organ. When there is the presence of insula lines, possible inflammatory masses or tumors should be taken into consideration. The application of this method in diagnosing and its combination with other methods are to be discussed in the following chapters.

Lines on the left palm are supposed to reflex one's congenital endowments which more often suggest one's past health condition, while those on the right palm are supposed to reflex postnatal acquirements which, more often, express and suggest one's present and future health conditions. Practice has shown that palmar lines representing some hereditary diseases such as diabetes are mostly present on the left hand. In examining the colors of palmar lines, the method of employing "the left hand for a man and the right hand for a woman" is usually applied.

Meanwhile, attention should be paid to the fact that palmar lines of both hands are related to the locations of the internal organs. For instance, diseases of the heart and the stomach can mostly be identified on the left hand, while liver diseases, mostly on the right hand. However, whatever disease it may be, if it shows pathologic lines symultaneously on both hands, the diagnosis can be confirmed beyond any doubt. Furthermore, both hands are respectively divided into the left side, betokened with the thumb, and the right side, betoked with the little finger. Diagnosing with this method can sometimes accurately determine the focus of the patient, such as in the lungs on which side or in the oviducts on which side. However, all the above-mentioned judgements have to resort to skilled practice and dexterous application of the methods in diagnosing through observing palmar lines.

Chapter Four   The Lines of the Palm and
Their Corresponding Diseases

I . The Fourteen Lines on the Palm

There are on the palm altogether 14 lines, of which 3 are main lines and 11 are auxiliary lines. For the sake of convinience, the 14 lines are numbered in the book with Arabian figures in a uniform sequence. Following is an introduction of the 14 lines respectively:

Line 1: alternately known as the remote ending horizontal curving line; the horizontal curving line under the root of the little finger; the emotion line; or the heaven line (see Fig. 12).

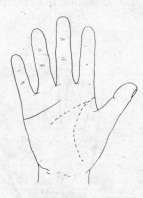

Fig. 12

Line 2: alternately known as the near ending horizontal curving line; the small thenar parabolic line; the brain line; or the human line(see Fig. 13).

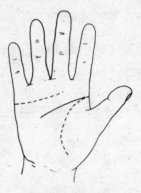

Fig. 13

Line 3: alternately known as the large thenar curving line; the large thenar parabolic line; the life line; or the earth line(see Fig. 14).

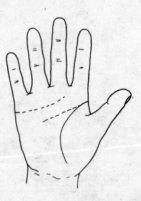

Fig. 14

Line 4: alternately known as the health line (see Fig. 15).

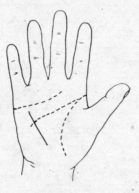

Fig. 15

Line 5: alternately known as the Jade Column line (see Fig. 16).

Fig. 16

Line 6: alternately known as the interference line (see Fig. 17).

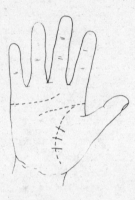

Fig. 17

Line 7: alternately known as the sun line (see Fig. 18).

Fig. 18

Line 8 : alternately known as the indulging line (see Fig. 19).

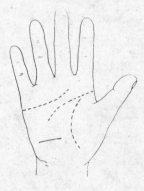

Fig. 19

Line 9 : alternately known as the Venus line (see Fig. 20).

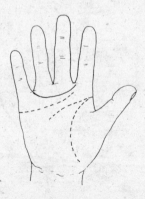

Fig. 20

Line 10: alternately known as the Saturn line (see Fig. 21).

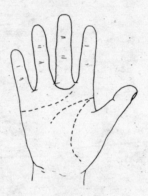

Fig. 21

Line 11: alternately known as the sexual line (see Fig. 22).

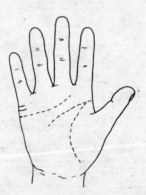

Fig. 22

Line 12: alternately known as the liver disease line or the drinking line (see Fig. 23).

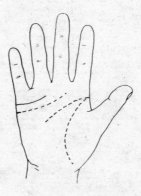

Fig. 23

Line 13: (see Fig. 24).

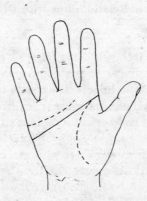

Fig. 24

Line 14: alternately known as the channeling line (see Fig. 25).

Fig. 25

II . Features of the Palmar Lines and Their Relationships with Diseases

1. Line 1

Line 1 runs from the ulnar muscles of the palm and the root of the little finger to the point under the gap between the index and middle fingers. It extends forward in the form of an arc or parabola. Its normal length should be that it reaches right the gap between the index and middle fingers. Its normal should be deep, long, distinct, clear and rosy with fewer branches downward but with more branches or auxiliary lines upward. It should not have straight intercepting lines and small insular or chain-like lines (see Fig. 26).

The length and trend of Line 1 reflect conditions of the function of the digestive system. One who wears an excessively long Line 1, which terminates at the lower edge of the articular cavity of the third segment of the index finger, tends to suffer from gastrointestinal vegetative nerve functional disturbance (see Fig. 27), while one whose Line 1

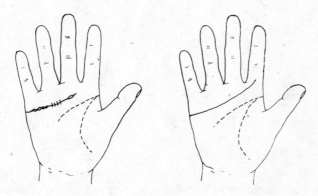

Fig. 26   Fig. 27

takes a sudden turn from under the middle finger into the gap between the index and middle fingers suggests that he has suffered from stomach trouble ever since his childhood (see Fig. 28). One who has a Line 1 which bears symultaneously both features mentioned above usually shows that he has a feeble function of the stomach and unsound function of absorption and digestion (see Fig. 29). The section of Line 1 between the index and middle fingers chiefly reflects the function of the respiratory system. One who has, in this section, many disordered branching lines or several horizontally-intercepting vertical thin lines often suffers from chronic

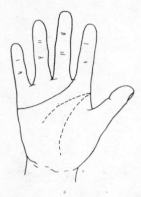 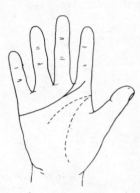

Fig. 28　　　　　　　**Fig. 29**

branchitis or branchiectasis (see Fig. 30).

Line 1 with small insular lines under the ring finger may be identified as abnormal in the eye and the optic nerve (see Fig. 31). Line 1 with large insular lines at its initial ending mostly indicates abnormal in the auditary nerve (see Fig. 32).

From the section of Line 1 ranging from under the ring finger to the little finger, conditions concerning the functions of the urinary and genital systems and the mammary glands may be observed.

Deformed breaking off of Line 1 suggests a poor function of the liver or former contraction of some serious disease in earlier years, which has caused changes in the immunity of the liver (see Fig. 33).

One whose Line 1 is intercepted by two vertical lines under the ring finger suggests an unstable blood pressure,

56

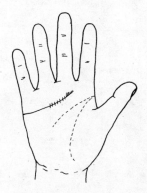

Fig. 30

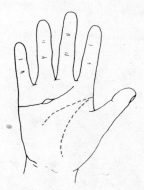

Fig. 31

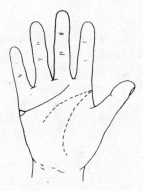

Fig. 32

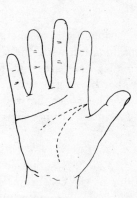

Fig. 33

while if there are fat prominences by both sides of the vertical line it mostly indicates that he suffers from hyperlipermia (see Fig. 34).

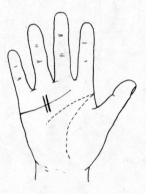

Fig. 34

Conditions of one's blood pressure should be judged in combination with one's acid and base areas: one who has a smaller base area but has a larger acid area usually has a higher blood pressure; otherwise, a lower one.

The space between Line 1 and Line 2 is known as "*Fangt'ing*,"whose narrowness suggests a poor vital capacity.

2. Line 2

Line 2 is supposed to have closely to do with the functions of the cerebrum and the nervous system, and that is why it is alternately known as "the brain line." Diseases it represents are mostly concerned with the nerves, the psyche and the cardiovascular system. Clinic observations have shown that this line may also reflect one's mentality and even one's external wound. The normal of Line 2 assumes the form of a parabola and is located at the center of the palm; it starts from the edge of the articular cavity of the third segment of the index finger, extends in the form of a parabola to the small thenar and terminates under the ring finger; it looks thick and long, distinct and unbroken, rosy in color and slightly drooping with possible branches near the edge of the palm.

Those who wear a standard Line 2 described as above are mostly healthy, full of vitality and high in spirits, while those who wear an excessively level and straight Line 2 may suggest their obstinacy and impetuousness (see Fig. 35).

Those whose Line 2 is netted with large insular lines often suggest that they suffer from vertigo or Meniere's disease (see Fig. 36).

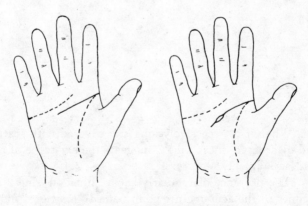

Fig. 35   Fig. 36

Those whose Line 2 is broken and intercepted by 2 or 3 branching lines at the center of the palm tend to have heart diseases (see Fig. 37) or congenital rheumatic heart disease.

The presence of several relatively distinct small insular lines at the point of intersection of Line 2 and Line 3 suggts one's malnutrition in his childhood (see Fig. 38).

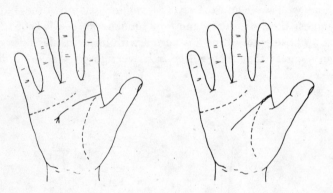

Fig. 37   Fig. 38

When it is excessively long and covered with scattering and disordered lines, Line 2 suggests the existence of neurosis (see Fig. 39).

The presence of regularly square lines on Line 2 in the vicinity of the acupuncture point named *"Laokung"* indicates an anamnesis of concussion of brain (see Fig. 40) or anameneses of general anesthesia, myelopathy or fracture of lumbar vertebra.

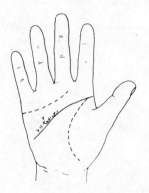 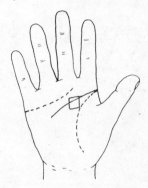

Fig. 39　　　　　　　　　　**Fig. 40**

The presence of square frames under the ring finger on
Line 2 often serves as marks of intestinal conglumination
remnant or external abdominal wound. (see Fig. 41).

The presence of distinct " + " -shaped lines on Line 2
suggests one's unstability of the psyche, arrhythmia or the
existence of recessive coronary heart disease (see Fig. 42). If
these square lines have grown into " * " -shaped lines, it is
mostly suggested that one suffers from vascular headache or
angina pectoris (see Fig. 43).

Most of the health conditions indicated by Line 2 are
hereditary and inherited, and the conditions of the heart and
the brain are chiefly presented by this line.

3. Line 3

Line 3 surrounds the whole globus of the thumb, and
forming a particular area, indicates conditions of man's constitution, energy, capability and health as well as diseases.

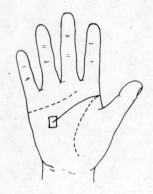

Fig. 41

Fig. 42

Fig. 43

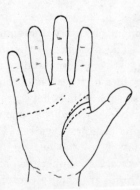

Fig. 44

That is why it is alternately known as "the life line." It is located at the middle point between the radicular lines of the roots of the index finger and the thumb, serving as the dividing line of the Mount of Jupiter and the First Mars Mount.

Those whose Line 3 takes a too low starting point are weak of their energy and takes a higher starting point tend to be staunch and resolute in character, vigorous of their liver-fire and often suffer from cholesystitis, while those whose Line 3 is feeble in their stomach and intestines (see Fig. 44).

One whose large thenar is excessively prominent and plump so much so that when looked levelly its composite fat can be seen tends to suffer from hyperlipoidemia, while one whose large thenar looks like cinnarba in color can be identified as a case of fatty liver. One who has a central straight line which extends from the center of the arc of the large thenar to the center of the middle finger mostly enjoys a good health (see Fig. 45).

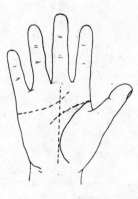

Fig. 45

The presence of insular lines on Line 3 indicates that one is more suscepfible to tumors than their presence on other lines.

The presence of " * "-shaped lines at the ending of Line 3 suggests a great probability of cerebrovascular accident, often of the type of sudden death. However, whatever lines one may have, as long as Line 3 runs through all these lines and extends downard, one has a chance to recover from his or her diseases. We should encourage the patient to build up confidence in his or her struggle to combat the disease.

One who has developed a protective line along the inner side of Line 3 generally suffers from irregulation of the intestinal tract, constipation or diarrhea, with constipation as the most common case. The presence of " * " -shaped lines or " # " -shaped on this protective line usually indicates enteritis or colitis (see Fig. 46).

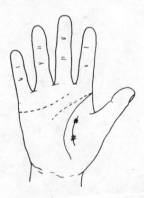

Fig. 46

If the area surrounded by Line 3 is very small, it is indicated that one has a poor health and one, either man or woman, is apt to suffer from dyspepsia or infertility (see Fig. 47).

One whose Line 3 looks plump and profound, becomes thinner and thinner gradually and finally disappears at its ending shows that he or she enjoys good health.

In observing Line 3, emphasis should be laid on the possible presence of " * " -shaped (see Fig. 48) or insular lines (see Fig. 49), or its abrupt breaking off (see Fig. 50), its extension on its halfway towards the Mount of the Moon (see Fig. 51), or its being cut through on its midway by intercepting lines. (see Fig. 52).

4. Line 4

Line 4 starts from the large thenar (standardized by its having not reached the curving line of the large thenar), ex-

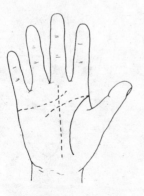

Fig. 47

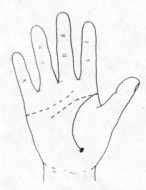

Fig. 48

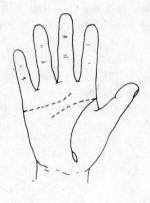

Fig. 49

Fig. 50

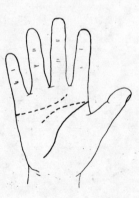

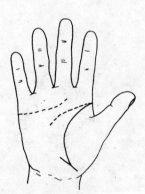

Fig. 51

Fig. 52

tends in an oblique direction toward the little finger and terminates right under the root of the little finger (see Fig. 53).

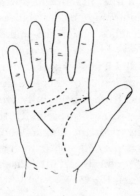

Fig. 53

One who enjoys good health rarely has such a line, which is commonly observed on the palm of a brain worker or a weak body. When pathologic changes take place within the body, Line 4 will keep deepening, but when health is recovered, it will become shallow again. Patients who suffer from a poor function of the liver or kidney or from chronic diseases in the respiratory system often wear a deep and distinct Line 4. Disconnecxion of Line 4 with Line 3 indicates freedom of severe diseases.

5. Line 5

Line 5 starts from the lower part of the palm, runs through the center of the palm (i. e. , the *mingt'ang*), and right reaches the line under the middle finger. It looks like an erective column on the palm, and that is why this line is alternately known as "the Jade Column line. " Unlike Lines

1, 2 and 3, Line 5 should not be too thick, and is preferably thin and shallow, straight upward, distinct and continuous and pink in its color. The changes of this line has to do with the health conditions. However, everybody does not necessarily wear such a line. Practice has proved that the presence of such a line is not a sign of healthiness, and the longer it is (so long as it reaches under the middle finger), a poorer health will it show, chiefly indicating a poor health in one's teens. A short Line 5 suggests that during the period represented by the appearance of this line, one's constitution declined but now health has been fully recovered. Chronic diseases signified by Line 5 are chiefly the weakening of the function of the heart or the lungs. Those who enjoy subjectively fine feelings may also wear such a line, whose presence indicates cardio-cerebral vascular diseases for middle-aged and old people (see Fig. 54).

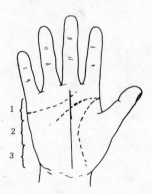

Fig. 54
1. old age   2. middle age   3. youth and teenage

6. Line 6

Line 6 is alternately known as the inerference line. The abnormal lines which intercept and cut through the main lines and some of the auxiliary lines are all known as interference lines. So, the location of Line 6 is flexible.

The presence on the large thenar of Line 6 which looks relatively deep and cuts into Line 3 by more than one cm. signifies that the person formerly suffered a severe disease at his or her corresponding age. The location at the upper end of Line 3 stands for childhood, while that at its lower end, for old age (see Fig. 55). The method of judging the time of one's case history is: draw parabolic lines from the gaps between the fingers, extend them parallelly with the lateral between the thumb and the index finger, and let them meet with Line 3; the area between the two curving lines is designated for one age group (see Fig. 56). By observing the presence of Line 6 in the respective areas, the age when one once

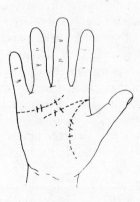

Fig. 55

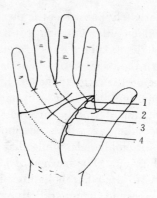

Fig. 56
1. 10—20 *years old* 2. 20—40 *years old*
3. 40—60 *years old* 4. 60—80 *years old*

suffered a disease can be judged and determined.

The presence of Line 6 on Line 2 or Line 1 should be analysed in combination with the relative locations of the lines. To be short, when Line 6 looks thin, short and shallow, there is not so much pathologic significance, while when it is deep and long (over 1 cm.), there is clinical significance.

At the connecting part of the areas designated as *Gen* and *Zhen* by the Eight Diagrams, the presence of one or two Lines 6 which are as deep as Line 3 and as long as two or three cm. in the form of dividing lines (see Fig. 57), with, at the same time, few and rare lines in the areas of *Gen* and *Zhen*, suggests the possibility that the patient has a tendency towards hemorrhage.

7. Line 7

Line 7, alternately known as the sun line, is a secondary line to Line 5. It is located under the ring finger and is shorter than Line 5. Clinically, this line is rarely seen, and the authoress has not yet found its particular clinic significance so far (see Fig. 58).

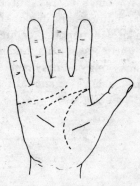

Fig. 57

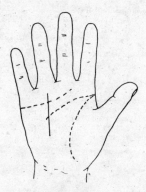

Fig. 58

8. Line 8

Line 8, alternately known as the indulging line, can be rarely found on the palms of ordinary people. The presence of such a line generally indicates the irregularity of life, long-term stay-up, overworking of the body and soul, excessive consumation of one's energy, or excessive and unrestrained sexuality, indulgement in smoking and drinking, or long-term taking-in of hyponotics or anesthetics. Line 8 is located in the slightly lower part under the Mount of the Moon. It looks thick, long and ugly, and extends toward Line 3. One who wears such a line should manage to change his bad habits in life (see Fig. 59).

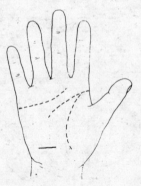

Fig. 59

9. Line 9

Line 9 is a curving line which runs from the lower edge of the gap between the index finger and the middle finger to the lower edge of the gap between the ring finger and the little finger (see Fig. 60). Those who wear such a line have mostly an alergic constitution.

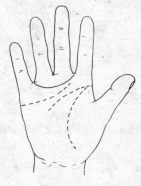

Fig. 60

For the past few years, there has been an increase in the number of people who wear such a line. It proves that the pollution by medicines and the atmosphere has led to the increase in the number of people who have an alergic constitution. Such a line can be found on the palms of both husband and wife who suffer from sterility. Hence, an examination of the sperm and the ovum and find out whether there are not antibodies which cause sterility.

10. Line 10

Line 10 is located at the root part of the middle finger and takes the form of a crescent (see Fig. 61). This line sig-

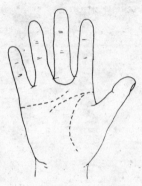

Fig. 61

nifies the stagnation of the liver-qi, and one's low spirits, and, at the same time, has to do with the family history of myopia.

11. Line 11

Line 11, alternately known as the sexual line, is a short line located at the 1/2 position above Line 1 (see Fig. 62). Most of the Chinese wear 2 or 3 such lines. If they look deep, level and straight, distinct and unbroken, and pink in color, they indicate that one has a normal function in his urinary and genital systems. If one has only one which is short or none Line 11, it indicates, for women, sterility, irregular menstruation or hypoplasia of uterus; and for men, azoospermia or sexual impotence. But if the line is excessively long and straightly extends toward the ring finger, it is indicated that one suffers from nephritis or prostatis. If there is the presence of " * " -shaped or interference lines, its clinical meaning would be greater (see Fig. 63).

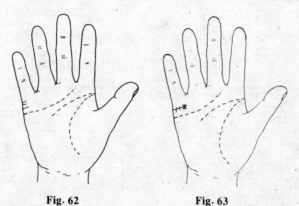

Fig. 62   **Fig. 63**

12. Line 12

Line 12, alternately known as the liver trouble line or the drinking line, starts from the middle part between Line 1 and the root line of the little finger, extends in parallel with Line 1 and terminates under the ring finger. For some peopel, it might be linked with Line 1 (see Fig. 64). Those who wear such a line are mostly abdicted to drinking or do not drink at all as they would be drunk even by drinking a small amount of wine, and as the detoxifying function of their liver is weekened, they often suffer from cirrhosis of the alcholism type. Those who have contacted some poisonous materials wear such a line, too. A deep and distinct Line 12 indicates a hepatic injury resulting from the poisoning which has intensified the loading of the liver. Line 12 can also be found on the palm of a patient of chronic hepatitis.

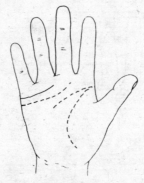

Fig. 64

13. Line 13

As a matter of fact, Line 13 is a variant of Line 2 which extends toward and reaches the lateral of the palm (see Fig. 65). It can be found on the palms of quite a number of children who are retarted in growth, impeted in study or abnormal in behavior. It can also be observed on the palms of those who suffer from cancer of the liver, hemotopathy and psoriasis. For some peopel, Line 13 is formed postnatally with Line 2 extending in a parabolic line form towards the lateral of the palm. The presence of insular lines on Line 13 is significant clinically, while the existence of a space between the starting points of Line 13 and Line 3 is more significant clinically (see Fig. 66).

14. Line 14

Line 14 is alternately known as the channeling line (see Fig. 67). A palm with the disappearance of Line 1 and the

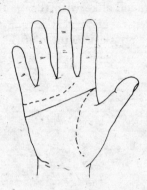

Fig. 65

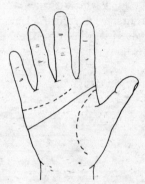

Fig. 66

Fig. 67

sole presence of Line 13 and Line 3 is known as a "channeled palm," or "the ape line." Health conditions Line 14 suggests are mostly hereditary, i. e. , the constitution, mentality, life expetancy and diseases are all much alike with those of the parents. Therefore, Line 14 represents a very strong tendendy towards inheritance in the physical features of the human body.

Chapter Five Changes of the Palmar Lines and Abnormal Lines Commonly Encountered

I . The Growth and Decline of Palmar Lines

The dynamic changes of the palmar lines can be briefly described as "sinking," "rising," "disappearing" and "growing."

The word "sinking" means deepening. As is known, the three main lines, i. e. , Line 1, Line 2 and Line 3, are the deepest and thickest ones. For normal persons, Line 1 and Line 3 are deeper and thicker than Line 2, and the initial end of each of these lines is deeper than the ending. If lines which ought to be deep have now become shallow or those which ought to be shallow have now become deep, it is indicated that some change or changes have taken place within the body. If an auxiliary line has become almost as deep as or even deeper than the main lines, it must be realized that a variation has taken place in the internal organ represented by the given auxiliary line. However, every of such variations is not necessarily caused by diseases, for it also may indicate conditions after recovery, when lines may have become either deeper or shallower. We have to deal with different cases in different ways. For instance, the deepening in the ending of Line 3 suggests the strengthening of vitality, but if it has become excessively deep with the presence of branches or insular lines, it may suggest the on-going struggle between the vital energy and the pathogenic factors or the worsening of the case. Those who wear an excessively deep Line 2 mostly suffer from headaches, while those whose Line 2 is excessively shallow usually suffer from headaches, too. So, preferably, the depth and the thickness of the lines are proper and moderate, for both excession and inadequacy are expressions of variations. For another example, after a surgical operation, there around the " * " -shaped pathologic lines will appear "□" -shaped lines, which, if looking deep, indicate an on-going formation of the scar at the part once operated on; if they have become shallower or even have disappeared, indicate a fine operative union; and, if they keep on deepening, indicate usually a partial conglumination or a recurrence of the old disease. Hence, deepening is none other than the dynamic form of the lines, and never should anybody take it one-sidedly as an omen of auspiciousness or inauspiciousness.

The word "rising" means becoming shallower. Generally, shallow lines suggest a light case or one in its initial stage or in the process of successful recovering. However, attention must be paid to the trend of the "rising": if it tends toward disappearing, it is indicated that the disease will be removed, but if it tends toward deepening, it is indicated that the case is becoming severer.

Generally, the endings of both the main lines and the auxiliary lines all should be shallower than their initial ends. Such is a normal state. But if their initial ends are "rising," it suggests a bad omen, while their deepening suggests a good trend. If the initial ends are rising until they have reached their endings and disappear there, a poor constitution is indicated. What is very particular is Line 3: whenever it rises, it indicates that some change has taken place. Only Line 4 is best when it becomes shallower.

The word "disappearing" means being no longer seen. Palmar lines may disappear, while creases, once formed, will never disappear. So, the term "disappearing" is applied for only lines not for creases. The small and thin lines on the palm appear and disappear now and then, and, generally, their disappearance indicates the removal of the disease. Through long-term observations of a number of patients of cholelithiasis, it has been discovered that when the " * " -shaped lines have shrunk back into " # " -shaped lines and some " + " -shaped lines have disappeared, it is confirmed clinically that the cholelithiasis has been alleviated or cured. Hence, "disappearing" is a good omen.

The word "growing," meaning increase, may be applied either with newly formed lines or with lengthened lines. As is known, lines can be newly emerging. When one is constantly in an unstable mood or being constantly and excessively fatigued, on his palm may newly emergy many a small and thin line, which after having formed, may either disappear or remain for a long time. Meanwhile, the main lines and the auxiliary lines may extend themselves or develop branches between them, thus having themselves being linked up. After a long period of growth, the small lines may grow into lines shallower than the original.

In addition, it is a frequent occurrence that " + " -shaped lines grow into " # " -shaped or " * " -shaped lines.

In observing palmar lines and creases, emphasis should be laid on their dynamic forms and trends, based upon which we judge and determine the seriousness, development and curing of diseases. The rate of accuracy in diagnosing by observing palmar lines is in direct proportion to the success in capturing the changes of the lines and creases such as sinking, rising, disappearing and growing.

II. The Eight Abnormal Lines Commonly Encountered

Generally, the presence of abnormal lines on the palm suggests some pathologic significance. The living environments and dietary habits among different ethnic groups and nationalities at different localities as well as their hereditary genes, diseases, constitutions, the capability of anti-diseases, the duration of illness and the changeable factors in the duration of illness, etc. are all different, and therefore, abnormal lines these factors have presented on the palm are naturally in a great variety. In my long-term clinic practice as a physician, I have epitomized 8 major abnormal lines, the respective presence of which in a given area usually indicates that some pathologic change has taken place in the corresponding part of the body.

1. The " * " -shaped Lines

Mostly, " * "-shaped lines or " * "-shaped variants consist of 3 or 4 short lines. Their presence suggests the existence of the stagnancy of the qi^1 and blood stasis in some internal organ. When they emerge in the gallbladder area, a case of cholelithiasis is indicated, while their emerging in the heart area predicates the occurrence of angina pectoris and forecasts a long duration of illness and a serious case. An identification and analysis of practical cases can be seen in Fig. 68 and Fig. 69.

2. The "+" -shaped Lines

They consist of 2 short lines or one shorter line and another longer line. A regular cross means more than an oblique cross. The "+"-shaped lines indicate the irregulation of the function of some internal organ or the occurrence of inflammation in some portion of the body. Compared with

Fig. 68

Fig. 69

the " $*$ "-shaped lines, the "$+$"-shaped lines suggest a lighter case and in its initial stage or indicates that the patient is on the mend and the disease will be removed.

An identification and analysis of practical cases can be seen in Fig. 70.

3. The Triangle Lines

They consist of 2 or 3 short lines, which join the main lines. Generally, they suggest a hidden danger of the occurrence of coronary heart diseases. But they signify a lighter case than the " $*$ " -shaped lines do and a more serious case than the "$+$" -shaped lines do. They possibly tend to grow into " $*$ " -shaped lines.

For practical cases to identify and analyse, see Fig. 71.

4. The Insular Lines

Insular lines assume the form of an island, and their scope and range may be large or small, separate or continuous, or overlapping. Therefore, they must be identified carefully. Usually, insular lines suggest the existence of tumor or inflammatory mass. The smaller they are, the greater their meaning will be. Excessively large insular lines tell only a feeble function of the internal organ represented by its corresponding area.

For practical cases to identify and analyse, see Fig. 72.

5. The Ringlike Lines

Such lines look like a ring, with additional disordered lines within the ring. Only when they are observed as a whole, can they be identified. Such lines belong to the rarely-seen type. In clinical observation, the authoress once observed such lines and found that they have to do with external wounds. Generally, those who have received serious external wounds often wear ringlike lines on their palms.

For practical cases to identify and analyse, see Fig. 73.

6. The " $\#$ " -shaped Lines

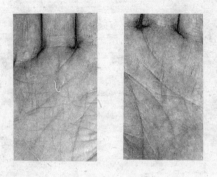

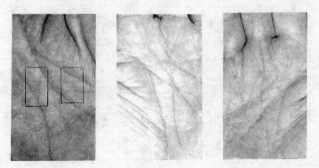

Fig. 70

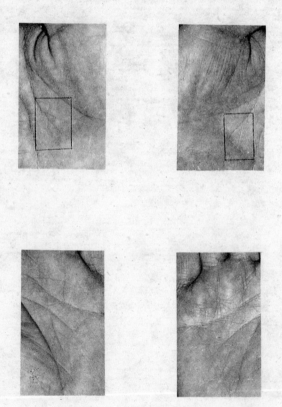

Fig. 71

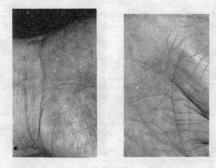

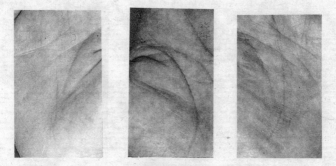

Fig. 72

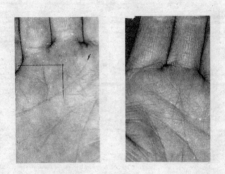

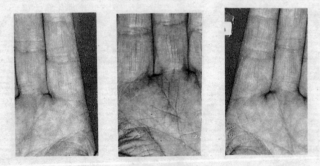

Fig. 73

Such lines assume a quadrilateral form and consist of 4 short lines. In their development, they may grow into " * " —shaped lines or may co-exist with" * "—shaped lines. Generally, they have to do with chronic inflammatory diseases and indicate a long duration of illness in a slow change and with a possible occurrence of a substantial change. Their presence in the gallbladder area suggests the existence of inflammation but without calculus.

For practical cases to identify and analyse, see Fig. 74.

7. The Square Lines

Square Lines consist of 4 short lines and assume the form of a rectangle or a square. They are signs indicating various scars left behind, for instance, by surgical operations or external wounds.

For practical cases to identify and analyse, see Fig. 75.

8. The Stellate Lines

Such lines bear the form of a five-pointed star and can be encountered rarely. Mostly, they suggest some pathologic change by inschemic cerebrovascular, which usually takes place in patients among the age group of 50 to 60 and shows extremely high rate of hemiparalysis. But conditions of such patients are generally fine after recovery, with a relatively low rate of mortality.

For practical cases to identify and analyse, see Fig. 76.

A co-existence of all the above-mentioned 8 kinds of lines may be found, symultaneously, on a single person's palm, or 1 or 2 kinds are found. However, as a matter of fact, the common presence of all of these lines in clinical practice is often mixed, crisscrossing, mutually connected and overlapping. For instances, there are " * " —shaped and/or" # "-shaped lines inside ringlike lines; there are horizontal and/or "+" —shaped lines inside insular lines; and there are "+"—shaped and/or" × "—shaped lines inside square lines.

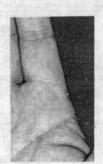

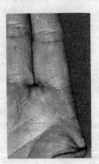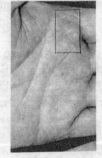

Fig. 74

Fig. 75

Fig. 76

Therefore, one must be very careful in observing and examining the lines and try to differentiate which is primary from which is secondary. The principle for the differentiation should be: to base ourselves upon the entirety rather than the parts; upon the deeper lines rather than the shallower ones; and upon the larger lines rather than the smaller ones; and always lay emphasis on the examination of their trends toward disappearing or growing. That is because obvious and distinct lines suggest that some diseases have already taken place and it is not easy to recover from them, while deep, small and thin lines indicate that the disease has just begun to invade the body or that the patient has not yet any subjective symptoms. Some lines, still during the period when the disease has already been removed but their corresponding lines remain, only serve for reference and do not have any true clinical significance. Some lines which have become indistinct, shallower and light-colored or even have almost disappeared show that the harm of the old disease to the body is disappearing, signifying that one suffered from some kind of disease in the past. Lines which have turned from being shallow and lightly colored into distinction or show an increase in their number, length and/or depth always indicate that the disease is worsening, and never should it be ignored and overlooked. For example, if "+" -shaped lines are observed in the heart area with newly formed disordered lines around it, it should be called to mind that the "+"-shaped lines may grow into " * "-shaped lines and that the patient tends to develop angina pectoris. So it is necessary to warn the patient of the necessity to take preventive measures.

It would take a long time to probe and experiment before one can accurately diagnose through observing and examining palmar lines, for it demands repreated analyses and judgements through a process of over and over again eliminating the false and retaining the true and discarding the dross and selecting the essential, so that, step by step, pathologic changes in the human body can be accurately determined and revealed.

Note:

The term *"qi"*, in traditional Chinese medical science, has the following three meanings:

a. it refers to vital energy, the refined nutritive substance flowing within the body, such as *qi* (essence) of water and food, and the inspired air;

b. it refers to the functional activity, generally denoting the function of the internal organs and tissues, e. g. , *qi* of the five solid viscera and *qi* of the six hollow viscera; and

c. it refers to one of the affected phases or stages in acute febrile disease.

Chapter Six   Diagnoses of Commonly Encountered Diseases through Observing Palmar Lines and Other Physical Features

Colds

Colds generally fall into two types:common cold and influenza.

The pathogens of common cold are rhinovirus, ECHO virus, Coxsackie virus, RS virus, adenovirus and so on. With cases of adults, rhinovirus is the chief pathogenic factor, while with cases of children, parainfluenza virus and RS virus. In traditional Chinese medicine, this disease is known as "invasion by the wind."

1. Main Points for the Diagnosis of Common Cold

a. The onset of common cold is rather acute, with apparent partial symptoms, such as nasal obstruction, running nose, sneezing, drily itching and sore throat, hoarseness, and tussiculation.

b. There are such possible symptoms as low fever, acratia, anorexia and pantalgia.

Influenza (flu for short) is an acute respiratory infectious disease caused by influenza virus, which is highly infectious and mainly spreads through droplet transmission. It consists of three types: A, B, C, of which virus Type A has frequent antigenic variation. The population's immunodeficiency to the variant virulent strain leads to the pandemicity of the disease. In traditional Chinese medicine, the disease is known as "influenza."

2. Main Points for the Diagnoses of Influenza

a. This disease shows an abrupt onset with slight partial

symptoms and distinct general symptoms of intoxication, which is symptomized as high fever, chilliness, pantalgia, headache, pain in the chest and back, cough and acratia.

b. There is a herd attack and contact history.

c. During the epidemic period, the disease is also characterized either by cough, expectoration and pectoralgia or by nausea, vomiting and diarrhea.

3. Clinical Types

a. The Type of Simple Form: it is symptomized by high fever (up to 40℃), chilliness, general malaise, lumbago, cephalagia (especially in the forehead, eyeballs and the posterior cervical region). When the general symptoms and high fever have extincted, symptoms of the respiratory system become obvious. Clinically, this type is most commonly encountered.

b. The Type of Pneumonia: it shows a persistent high fever, short of breath, cyanosis, paroxysmal cough, and hemoptysis. The duration of illness may last for 3 or 4 weeks. The patient registers a low rate of blood counting and neutropenia. An X-ray examination may show flocculent shadows in both lungs.

c. The Type of the Central Nerve: it is characterized by obvious symptoms of the central nervous system, which include persistent high fever, severe headache, vertigo, delirium or even coma; there may also occur meningeal irritation, stiff-neck and positive reaction in a straight leg raising test.

d. The Type of the Stomach and Intestine: it chiefly shows gastrointestinal symptoms such as nausea, vomiting, abdominalgia and diarrhea.

4. Methods of Diagnosis

The Color and Luster of the Palm

With a case of common cold, the patient looks pale in the palm with cold finger tips and visible blue contours of blood vessels. The wrist shows bulging contours of blood vessels, and the area designated as *Gen* bears a dark-blue color.

With a case of influenza, the palm shows a mixed color of red and pale, and the area designated as *Gen* looks darkly blue (see Fig. 77).

The Palmar Line

If a person suffers from a common cold or influenza accompanied by pneumonia or bronchitis, there will be an apparent increase in the number of Line 1, and at the same time, there may be the presence of small, thin and disordered lines in the areas designated as *Qian* and *Dui* (see Fig. 78).

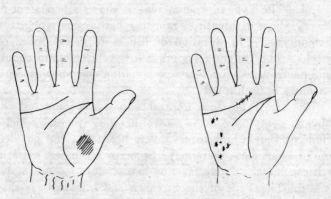

Fig. 77   Fig. 78

If a case of influenza is accompanied by gastrointestinal symptoms, the area designated as *Gen* will become prominent and show a red color. In the early stage of the disease, the area designated as *Zhen* will show no apparent changes, but with the occurrence of anacatharsis, it may become sunken, flaccid in the muscles and pale in color (see Fig. 79).

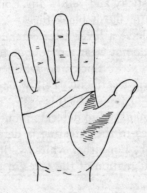

Fig. 79

The Nail

The nail body gives out a red hue, and with cases of high fever, the nail margins may become crimson.

The Tongue

With a case of common cold, the texture of the tongue is light in color either with thin fur or without fur at all.

During the early stage of influenza or during the initial period of fever, the tongue looks red, particularly the tongue tip. The fur is white in color and thick at the root of the tongue, or it is sticky and white or yellow.

During the middle stage of influenza when the fever does not abate, the tongue usually becomes purple, the fur turns from white to yellow, and the fur at the root of the tongue is sticky and yellow.

If the influenza is accompanied with gastrointestinal symptoms, the tongue proper is relatively normal but the fur looks sticky, yellow and thick.

If the influenza shows symptoms of the central nervous system, the patient will have a dark purple tongue covered fully and thickly with snow-white fur that cannot be wiped off, or by thick, sticky and yellow fur. Sometimes, such cases may wear brown or burnt-black fur.

Those who have a fever after catching a cold can easily be cured if they do not wear any tongue fur or only thin fur, while those who wear thick and white tongue fur usually need a longer-term treatment. Yellow or dark-brown fur indicates retention of feces. In this case, the stagnant excrement should be managed to defecate immediately. As soon as the stagnant feces in the intestine is defecated, the tongue fur will disappear. For either white, yellow or black fur has to do with the stagnation of the feces in the intestine.

The Lip

During the middle and late stages of influenza, herpes labialis may occur. The presence of herpes on the left labial corner is often concomitant with inflammation of the lesser curvature of the stomach, while that on the right labial corner is often concomitant with inflammation of the greater curvatrue of the stomach. The presence of herpes on the upper lip is often concomitant with colitis, constipation or diarrhea. The presence of herpes in the middle of the upper lip, for cases of the female sex, indicates the invasion of the blood chamber by heat, which will necessarily result in menorrhagia and irregular menstrual period. Or, the cold will cause pelvic inflammation, which will result in leukorrhagia, underbelly pain, etc. (see Fig. 80).

The Eye

With a case of influenza, both eyes seem to contain

Fig. 80

teardrops with the existence of red blood streaks on the conjunctivae (see Fig. 81)。

Fig. 81

The Tooth

With a case of influenza, if there is the presence of a red line on the patient's gum margin, it is known as "Francke's symptom," which indicates an internal Vc deficiency.

The Ear

With a case of common cold, both ears often look white without otic angiectasis.

With a case of influenza, the ears look red. If red veins bulge out at the acupoints for the stomach and abdomen on the ear, it indicates that the influenza has caused apparent pathologic changes in the gastrointestinal tract, such as nausea, vomiting, abdominalgia and diarrhea (see Fig. 82). With a child case, if it has a fever at the roots of the ears and chilliness at the tips of the ears, its body temperature will be over 38℃。

Fig. 82

Migraine

Migraine is a clinical syndrome that is caused by complicated pathogenic factors with a higher rate of occurrence among the female sex. It is manifested by periodical and paroxysmal headaches, which are mostly unilateral and tend to be hereditary. In traditional Chinese medicine, it belongs to the category of "headaches due to blood stasis."

1. Main Points for Diagnosis

a. This disease often occurs around adolenscence and the attack is often related to the menstrual cycle.

b. Periodically attacking headaches share a similar process.

c. With some such cases, before the attack of the headache, there are usually temporary premonitory symptoms such as lassitude, lethargy, discomfort and dysopia (amaurosis, visual hallucination, hemianopsia, flash blindness and scotoma).

d. The ache in most cases is located in the forehead, the temples and the orbits. It is often unilateral, while with a few cases, it is bilateral. Manifested as distending, drilling or jumping pain, the headache may last several hours or several days or with a possible interval for several days or several months.

e. There may also show gastrointestinal and vegetative nervous symptoms, such as nausea, vomiting, headache, and unilateral congestion of both the conjunctivae and the nasal mucosa as well as lacrination and running nose.

2. Methods of Diagnosis

The Color and Luster of the Palm

A case of migraine usually has red palms or palms evenly dotted with red and white spots. Among cases of middle-aged women, an attractive red color may be observed in the small thenar (see Fig. 83).

Bulging blue contours of blood vessels can be seen in the wrist, and the area designated as *Gen* bears a bluish pale color (see Fig. 84).

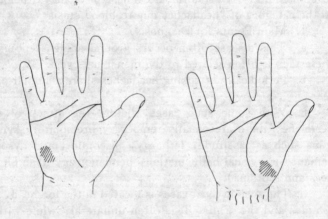

Fig. 83   Fig. 84

The Palmar Line

a. Line 2 is straight with " * "-shaped lines or cocking-up thin lines (see Fig. 85).

b. The second segment of the index finger is short with " * " -shaped lines (see Fig. 86).

C. Those with channeled palms tend to develop migraine (see Fig. 87).

d. Those who have two parallel Health Lines tend to develop migraine (see Fig. 88).

e. Those whose thumbs assume the forms of round balls

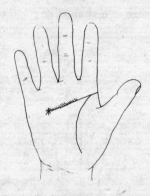

Fig. 85

Fig. 86

Fig. 87

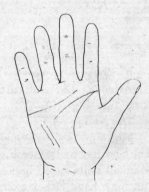

Fig. 88

tend to deuelop migraine (see Fig. 89).

f. Those who wear no other lines except the three main lines tend to get migraine.

g. Those whose Line 2 appears in a chain-like form tend to get migraine (see Fig. 90).

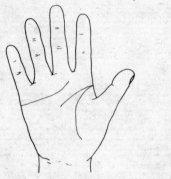 

Fig. 89   **Fig. 90**

h. Those who wear a short line branching from the area designated as *Dui* and cutting into Line 2 tend to get migraine (see Fig. 91).

The Nail

Migraine is often encountered among those who wear plane and flat nails (see Fig. 92), square nails (see Fig. 93) and small nails (see Fig. 94) with ridges (see. Fig. 95). The nails may have either excessively large semilunar flaps or have none at all, but they all show a blue color at their roots (see Fig. 96).

The Tongue

104

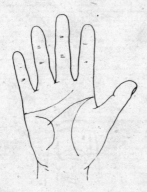

Fig. 91

Fig. 92

Fig. 93

Fig. 94

Fig. 95   **Fig. 96**

Generally, the tongue is coated with thin and white fur, while the texture of the tongue looks red with visible blood stasis in the lingual margins.

The Nose

One whose nose bridge inclines toward the left is susceptible to migraine on the right side, and vice versa.

The Eye

The contours of red blood vessels can be observed in the upper right part of the eyeball (see Fig. 97).

The Facial Expression

The facial color of a case of migraine is often pale mixed with blue. The patients often wear two or three vertical wrinkles at the acupoint Yint'ang with relatively distinct eye-corner wrinkles.

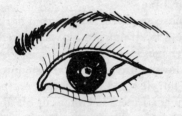

Fig. 97

Apoplexy (Cerebrovascular Accident and Cerebral Hemorrhage)

Customarily, people tend to regard such diseases as hemiparalysis, faint and facial paralysis as "apoplexy." Actually, by the so-called apoplexy are meant such symptoms as coma, clonic convulsion and hemiparalysis caused by cerebrovascular disease (cerebral hemorrhage, cerebral thrombosis, and cerebral embolism). Apoplexy not only registers a high rate of mortality but also causes severe sequels which can hardly be cured completely.

1. Premonitary Symptoms

a. If cases of hypertension or heart diseases show serious tortuous venous enlargement in their temples, it foretells the possible occurrence of apoplexy which causes hemiparalysis.

b. That the thumb bears no visible semilunar flap and that one often gets choked when drinking water indicate the probability to develop cerebral thrombus, while that the thumb wears an excessively large semilunar flap and that one often gets choked when drinking water indicate the susceptibility to cerebral hemorrhage.

2. Methods of Diagnosis

The Palmar Line

a. One whose small thenar shows a dark brown color, and whose Line 2 is straight in a parallel trend tends to get cerebral hemorrhage (see Fig. 98).

b. The following are premonitory symptoms of cerebral hemorrhage: a purplish red line appears on the radial lateral of the index finger; Line 3 is either cut off abruptly, disappears or is cut short by interference lines; or there is the formation of "△" -shaped or " * " -shaped lines (see Fig. 99, Fig. 100 and Fig. 101).

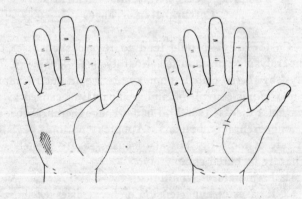

Fig. 98   Fig. 99

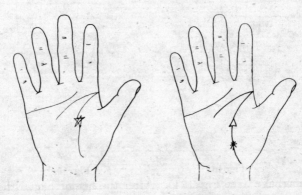

Fig. 100   **Fig. 101**

c. If scarlet red color can be observed on the skin surface of both the large and small thenars, it indicates that one is susceptible to hypertension and shows the symptoms of apoplexy and hemiparalysis, and this can be further confirmed by the sagging of the root of the middle finger or its dark purple color (see Fig. 102).

d. The presence of insular lines on Line 1 and the completeness and distinction of Line 2 and Line 3 suggest possible accidents caused by encephalic angioma or cerebrovascular malformation (see Fig. 103).

The Eye

If a hypertensive has mydriasis in both eyes and conjunctival congestion when looking obliquely towards the nose, it suggests an impending danger of cerebral

109

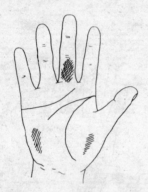

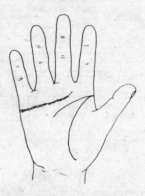

Fig. 102   **Fig. 103**

hemorrhage (see Fig. 104). After the hemorrhage, the eye on the side of the hemorrhage will look in an outward inclination and wrinkles will appear on the opposite side of the face (see Fig. 105).

The Tongue

With a case of apoplexy, the color of the patient's tongue root looks greyish black. The blue color in the tunica intima of the upper tip can serve as a premonitary symptom of apoplexy.

The Physical Feature

The consitutional type of cases of cerebral hemorrhage falls into the following two kinds:

a. Apoplectic type (alternately known as red sclerosis or primary BP hyperfunction): it is manifested by obesity (especially of the abdomen), macrocephaly, short neck, alopecia, flushed face, conjunctival congestion, raised shoulders, and

110

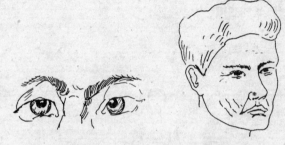

Fig. 104   **Fig. 105**

pyknic fingers. Those who are strong in their middle age
show a tendency toward the development of cerebral hemorrhage after 40 or 50 of age (see Fig. 106).

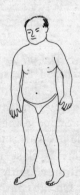

Fig. 106

b. Sclerotic type (alternately known as albinic sclerosis): this type is mainly encountered among cases of chronic gastritis and atrophic gastritis and is characterized by leanness, paleness, alopecia, bulging contours of blood vessels that feel sclerotic. This type of people are usually healthy but prone to get cerebral hemorrhage around the age of 60 to 70 (see Fig. 107).

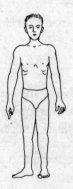

Fig. 107

Connexion between Blood Pressure and Cerebral Hemorrhage

The blood pressure of a healthy person is maintained within a certain range. Suppose the systolic pressure is 1, then the normal diastolic pressure should be 7/11 of it. If a person's diastolic pressure is close to 8/11 of the systolic pressure, he may be confronted with the possible occurrence of cerebral hemorrhage. On the contrary, if the pressure difference is too great and the proportion is up to 6/11, the person tends to have such diseases as cold, pneumonia, pulmonary tuberculosis, gastric ulcer and cancer.

Chronic Bronchitis

The pathogenic factors for chronic bronchitis are fairly complicated. It is a chronic nonspecific inflammation of the trachea, bronchial mucosa and the peripheral tissues due to a long-term interplay of external factors such as infection, physicochemical factors and alergia, and internal factors such as low defense function and immunologic function of the respiratory tract. Chronic bronchitis belongs to the category of cough with phlegm retention and dyspnea in traditional Chinese medicine.

1. Main Points for Diagnosis

a. Chronic bronchitis is mainly symptomized by cough and expectoration accompanied by gasp. The case can be confirmed if the attack lasts for about three months each year and occurs in succession for over two years, and, at the same time, the causes of the cough, expectoration and gasp are ruled out by possible cardinal or pulmonary diseases such as pulmonary tuberculosis, pneumoconiosis, bronchial asthma, bronchiectasis, lung cancer, heart disease, cardiac functional insufficiency, etc.

b. The onset and exacerbation of cough and expectoration are often in cold seasons and the expectoration is severer in the morning and in the evening. The sputum is white, sticky and frothy but turns into mucopurulent sputum if an acute onset is concomitant with bacterial infection. The cough is severer and the amount of expectoration increases, with possible high fever, short breath and/or gasp.

2. Clinical Types and Phases

a. Clinical Types:

(1) The simple type: the symptoms are identical with the diagnosis of chronic bronchitis, such as cough and expectoration but without asthma.

(2) The gasping type: the symptoms are identical with the diagnosis of chronic bronchitis such as cough, expectoration and gasp often with wheezes of asthma.

b. Clinical Phases:

(1) the acute attack phase: it refers to the occurrence of purulent and mucopurulent sputum and an evident increase in the amount of expectoration within one week's time concomitant possibly with inflammatory signs like fever and so on, or obvious exacerbation of either cough, expectoration or gasp.

(2) chronic persisting phase: the patient may suffer slight or severe cough, expectoration and asthma that may last for over one month.

(3) the clinic remission phase: this indicates that through treatment or self remission, most symptoms disappear, or there is occasionally a slight cough with a small amount of sputum that lasts for over two months.

3. Methods of Diagnosis

The Palmar Line

There is the presence of disordered lines in the area designated as *Dui* (see Fig. 108), while there is the presence of vertical lines on Line 1 (see Fig. 109). Bluish dark in color, the area designated as *Li* has bright and yellowish brown glossy prominence like ridges of friction. Line 9 may appear with cases of an allergic constitution (see Fig. 110).

The Nail

Cases of chronic bronchitis often wear long nails (see Fig. 111) with vertical ditches (see Fig. 112), especially the nails of the thumb and the index finger. With a prolonged case, the nails are often long and crooked (see Fig. 113) with

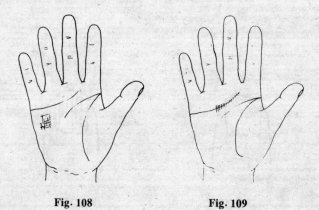

Fig. 108   Fig. 109

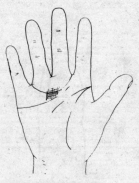

Fig. 110

115

Fig. 111

Fig. 112

Fig. 113

thick walls.

The Tongue

Cases of chronic bronchitis, when not attacked by the disease, often show a tongue light in color with thin and white fur; if the case is accompanied with expectoration, the fur is usually thick and sticky. During the phase of acute attack, the tongue bears a red or cyanotic color coated with greasy and white or greasy and yellow fur.

The sublingual veins become thicker and the sublingual mucosa turns red.

The Lip

With a prolonged case of chronic bronchitis complicated with pleuritis adhesion between the lip and the gum may be observed in the tunica intima of the upper lip. Excessive smoking of such cases may cause the presence of a large brown mottling of sediment in this portion.

The Facial Expression

With cases of chronic bronchitis, the skin at the acupoint Jenchung and on both laterals of the upper lip bears a dark-blue or pale color.

Those who have a feeble function of the respiratory system may have nares flaring and small nose with large nostrils. The nose is slightly cocking, or the nose is prominent with thin muscles.

The Eye

A patch of greyish blue shadow can be seen on the sclera in a child case.

The Neck

During the acute phase, prominences of veins can be observed in the neck.

Pneumococcus Pneumonia

Pneumococcal pneumonia is an acute pulmonary infection caused by streptococcus pneumoniae, and constitutes 90—95% of the disease incidence of bacterial pneumonia. This disease often occurs in winter and spring and is chiefly encountered among young and middle-aged people, who make up 40% of such cases. In traditional Chinese medicine it belongs to the category of wind-dampness syndrome, retention of pathogenic heat in the lung and cough.

1. Main Points for Diagnosis

a. It has an abrupt and vehement onset with such symptoms as shiver, high fever, pectoralgia, cough and rusty sputum.

b. No distinct physical features are shown in the early period. But with the occurrence of massive consolidation, intensified vocal fremitus and resonance can be heard in the area with pathologic change, and respiratory sound and moist rales can be heard in the bronchi.

c. Toxic pneumonia or shock pneumonia, besides showing the symptoms, physical features and X-ray signs of pneumonia, is mostly characterized by the failure of the peripheral circulation such as cold limbs, general cold sweat, cyanotic lips and nails, and the blood pressure is lower than 10.7/6.7 kPa or even immeasurable. Pneumonia of this type is commonly encountered among elderly and physically weak people, those who have suffered from heart or lung diseases or those whose resistance is generally or partially weakened.

2. Methods of Diagnosis

The Color and Luster of the Palm

a. The grayish dark color and lusterlessness of the palm

usually indicate organic hypoimmunity resulting from exopathic cold. Both the large and small thenars, the areas designated as *Kun* and *Li* and the area at the ring finger bear a scarlet red color, or patchy or flecked red color may be observed in these areas (see Fig. 114).

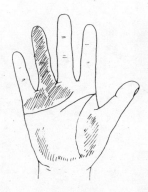

Fig. 114

b. The palm base feels hot, while the finger tips, cold.

c. The area designated as *Gen* often shows a bluish white color with visible contours of the blood vessels.

The Palmar Line

Feathery thin lines are often seen in a crisscross form on Line 1 (see Fig. 115). These lines may disappear after the recovery from pneumonia. But with some cases, due to the long duration of illness, "□" -shaped lines are formed on Line 1. If such lines are located approximately under the index finger, it suggests that the infected area is close to the apex and hilus of the lung; if they are located approximately under the ring finger or the little finger, it suggests that the

119

infected area is low in the lung. The existence of such lines on the right palm indicates that the right lung is infected and vice versa. Moreover, the symultaneous presence of such lines on both palms indicates, accordingly, that both lungs are infected symultaneously (see Fig. 116).

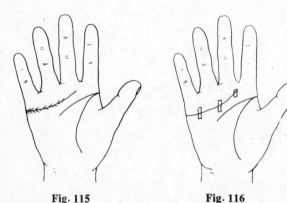

Fig. 115   Fig. 116

The Nail

Those with unhealthy lungs often wear long nails (see Fig. 117), especially on the index fingers. At the same time, the second segment of the index finger is often thin and feeble (see Fig. 118).

The Tongue

With a case of pneumonia, the lingual margins look red and the fur is so white that it seems as if the whole tongue were completely coated with a layer of white snow and it cannot be scraped away. When the fur turns yellow or dark brown, the tongue proper turns purple and a persistent high fever occurs with a case of pneumonia, it usually signifies

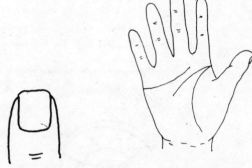

Fig. 117   Fig. 118

that there are in the intestinal canal stagnant feces, which
should be defecated as soon as possible. With the defecation,
the body temperature will drop.

The Lip

White lips with cheilosis indicate high fever and dehy-
dration, while lip ulcer indicates the improvement of the
case.

The Eye

With a child case of pneumonia, grey spots can be observed in the sclera of the eye (see Fig. 119). The eyeballs
are mostly bluish white, with possible presence of blood
streaks due to a persistent high fever.

The Ear

Cold in the tips of the ears and heat in their roots both
suggest that a high fever is difficult to abate; and that even
if the temperature drops down temporarily, it may go up

Fig. 119

again.

The Facial Expression

That the acupoint Yint'ang bears a white color indicates a slight case, while its blue color indicates a relatively severe case. Its black color suggests that the case is even severer, while its scarlet color signifies a persistent high fever.

The face is flushing due to the high fever, but the acupoint Yint'ang usually looks bluish pale with bulging contours of the veins in the temples and the same feature can be observed at the root of the nose. With a case of pneumonia of the shock type, the face generally bears a pale and blue color with cyanotic lips, and the limbs feel chilly with cold sweat. Those who tend to contract pulmonary and tracheal diseases usually wear a diamond-shaped face, protruding cheek bones, a slim and long spine, a perverted trapezoidal trunk, a thin thorax, an obtuse angular jaw and a narrow space between the pupils. After treatment when the case of pneumonia is controlled, the face will become moistly flushing, but excessive flushing of the face may indicate the pulmonary dysfunction. After recovering from pneumonia, the face may become small and pointed, and the insufficiency of the facial muscles and fat is a sign of pulmonary dysfunction. Those who are susceptible to pneumonia usually wear a small and pointed nose and a small little finger.

Pulmonary Emphysema

Pulmonary emphysema refers to the excessive expansion and aeration of the pulmonary alveoli, concomitant symultaneously with declining elasticity of the lung tissues, enlarged volume and impaired pulmonary function. This disease falls into four types: a. chronic obstructive (or hypertrophic) emphysema; b. senile (or atrophic) emphysema; c. localized emphysema; and d. compensatory emphysema. Obstructive emphysema can be initiated by disturbances of ventilation resulting from any diseases that can cause the inflammation of the bronchus, such as chronic bronchites, pneumonia, bronchial asthma, bronchiectasis and pulmonary fibrosis.

1. Chief Symptoms

The irritation of chronic bronchitis and the gradual accumulation of the secretion signify the process of pulmonary emphysema from quantitative change to qualitative change. The patient usually has a long case history of cough and expectoration with short breath as the chief symptom, which is slight during the early stage or occurs only after physical labor. With the advance of the disease, however, such a symptom becomes more and more obvious, as the patient may feel short of breath after slight activities or even in walking. With a severe case of pulmonary emphysema, coughing becomes more frequent and bronchial secretion increases in cold winter time. Concomitant infection of the respiratory tract may lead to aggravated hypoxia and even retention of carbon dioxide. Clinically, there will be such symptoms as worsened chest distress, exacerbation of short breath, cyanosis, headache, fast heart rate, lethargy and trance. Without a timely treatment, the case tends to develop into respiratory failure.

2. Methods of Diagnosis

The color and Luster of the Palm

During the attacking stage, the palm looks bluish white and during the stationary stage, it may turn red but still in a cyanotic appearance. The muscles of the palm are pulmp but flaccid and asthenic. All the mounts are prominent and rebound slowly when pressed down. The ten fingers look like drumsticks.

The Palmar Line

The space between Line 1 and Line 2 is evidently widened, that is, Line 1 has moved upwards and Line 2 downwards. Between the two lines, there is the existence of "+"-shaped lines or "×"-shaped lines (see Fig. 120). With some cases, Line 1 branches out under the middle finger a line which is cut through by some small vertical lines. The area designated as *Kan* is sagging and pale in color (see Fig. 121)

The Nail

The roots of the nails look purplish blue, and there are vertical stripes on the thumb nail. The nail of the index finger becomes long. Every nail props and wraps up the nail matrix like a sea shell, and they become long and hook-like, resembling the claw of an eagle (see Fig. 122).

Fig. 120

Fig. 121

Fig. 122

The Tongue

The tongue looks dark purple and is possibly coated with white or yellow and greasy fur. The sublingual veins turn thick in form and purple in color.

The Facial Expression

Such a patient often wears a "申" -shaped face with a short space between the eyes. The nostrils are large, and the lower eyelids are puffy. The lips look darkly purple, and cannot be put closely together even at ordinary times.

The Neck

Carotid pulsation is observable in the neck and the acupoint T'ient'u caves in. The depression on the clavicle is especially apparent when the patient is inspirating.

The Physical Feature

With such a case, the thorax assumes the form of a barrel, and the ribs and stomach are at a parallel level with a widened space between the ribs. The respiratory mobility attenuates and the vocal fremitus reduces. High resonance can be heard with a percussion examination.

Pulmonary Tuberculosis

Pulmonary tuberculosis is a chronic infectious disease caused by contracting Mycobacterium tuberculosis. The main source of infection is the tuberculous excreter's sputum and spray that are transmitted through the respiratory tract. In traditional Chinese medicine this disease belongs to the category of consumption.

1. Main Points for Diagnosis

a. General symptoms: a low fever in the afternoon, acratia, poor appetite, gradual loss of body weight and night sweat. Possible menstrual disorder and amenia are encountered often with female cases. A possible high fever may appear when the pulmonary focus is rapidly and vigorously advancing and disseminating.

b. Symptoms of the respiratory tract: generally, there is a dry cough, or one with only a small amount of sputum crudum. With a secondary infection, there may appear purulent sputum. With about one third of such cases are hemoptic by different degrees.

c. During the early stage of the case, there may be no abnormal physical features due to the fact that the pathologic change has taken place in a limited area or in the deep portion of the lung tisssues. But if a slightly dull sound is heard through a percussion examination in the area above or below the clavicle and the interscapular region and at the same time wet rales are heard when the patient is coughing, the case can be mostly identified as pulmonary tuberculosis.

2. Clinical Types

a. Primary pulmonary tuberculosis (TB Type I): when a person's resistance reduces, the inspiration of infectious Mycobacterium tuberculosis will cause exudative inflammatory focus in the lungs, resulting in lymphangitis and lymphnoditis. That is why primary focus in the lung, lymphangitis and regional lymphnoditis are generally known as primary syndrome. Tuberculosis of this type is chiefly encounterd among children. The symptoms are often slight and transient and can be automatically absorbed and calcificated.

b. Hematogenous pulmonary tuberculosis (TB Type II): it is often developed from primary pulmonary tuberculosis. But with adults, this disease is more often initiated by the dissemination of bacteria through blood after the diabrasis of the secondary intrapulmonary or extrapulmonary foci.

(1) Acute miliary pulmonary tuberculosis: there is often an acute onset; the patient has general intoxicated symp-

toms, often accompanied by tubercular meningitis; through an X-ray examination, intrapulmonary foci like grains of millet can be seen disseminating across the lungs unevenly.

(2) Subacute or chronic hematogenous pulmonary tuberculosis: there is no evident clinical symptom of intoxication, and the advance of the case is slow; the roentgenograph may show that the intrapulmonary foci, different in size and stage, are distributed across the upper and middle regions of the lungs.

c. Infiltrative pulmonaty tuberculosis (TB Type Ⅲ): secondary pulmonary tuberculosis is often found as of the infiltrative type and among adults. The clinical symptoms may vary with the difference in the foci's property and extent and human body's reactions. If the foci are located above and below the clavicle, the roentgenoghaph may show patchy and flocculent shadows without distinct margins.

d. Chronic fibro-cavitative pulmonary tuberculosis (TB Type Ⅳ): when the pulmonary tuberculosis is not discovered in time or not treated properly, the cavities will exist for a long time, so that the cavitary paries will become gradually thicker and extensive fibrosis will be found in the foci; consequently, with the fluctuation of the body's immunity, the absorption, repair and exacerbation of the foci occur alternately, and this is widely known as chronic fibro-cavitative pulmonary tuberculosis. Clinically, the duration of illness becomes persistent, and the symptoms become distinct or indistinct now and then. The patient's sputum, often with Mycobacterium tuberculosis, serves as the source of infection. Roentgenograph shows that a single or multiple thick-walled cavities appear on one or both lungs, often concomitant with bronchogenic disseminating foci and evident pleural thickening.

e. Tuberculous pleurisy (TB Type V): it is a disease often encountered among children and youths and initiated by the invasion of Mycobacterium tuberculosis into the pleural cavity. During its initial stage, it is dry (or fibrinous) pleurisy. But when the inflammation is further developed, serous fluid will exudate and gradually become exudative pleurisy. Such a diagnosis can be confirmed through an X-ray examination or a diagnostic pleuracentesis.

3. Methods of Diagnosis

The Color and Luster of the Palm

The area under the ring finger and the little finger is dark and lusterless. In the early period of infection, the regional color is brightly red and gradually turns darker and lighter with the advance of the disease and finally becomes grey after the healing of the focus. Generally, the area under the little finger indicates the location of the focus in the left lung, while that under the ring finger indicates that in the right lung (see Fig. 123). The lungs' condition can be observed through examining the areas designated as *Kun*, *Qian* and *Gen*. If these areas are normal in color and are spread with white lesser tubercles (see Fig. 124), this indicates the healing of the disease. Calcified pulmonary tuberculosis may be manifested as local and permenant blue spots in these areas, the palm as a whole dark in color and lusterless or spread with punctate grey alternating with white. With some male cases, purplish red papules that feel hard when palpated may appear on the back of the fingers like grains of soybean in size, and the ring finger tends to be stiff and clumsy with the second segment of the index finger becoming thinner.

The Palmar Line

a. Line 1 is disordered and cut through by "□"-shaped lines. The presence of the "□"-shaped lines at the middle of Line 1 signifies the location of the focus at the hilus of the

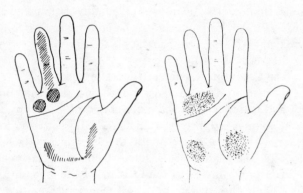

Fig. 123   **Fig. 124**

lung; while the presence at the front end of Line 1 suggests the location at the apex of the lung. If the "☐"-shaped lines appear under the little finger, it indicates the location of the focus at the lower part of the lung often with pleural adhesion or metastasis of the tuberculosis to abdominal viscera (see Fig. 125).

b. The presence of relatively large "☐"-shaped lines at the mid-upper section of Line 3 indicates that the patient once contracted severe pulmonary tuberculosis and pleural tuberculosis (see Fig. 126). At the same time, Line 1 may be cut short by plumose thin stripes, while Line 3 is also intercepted (see Fig. 127).

c. Lines known as "disease-contracting lines" emerge on the second segment of the index finger from the palmaris to the dorso-ventral boundary of the hand. The presence of dark purple spots on such lines usually indicates the existence of a focus of an old pulmonary tuberculosis (see Fig. 128).

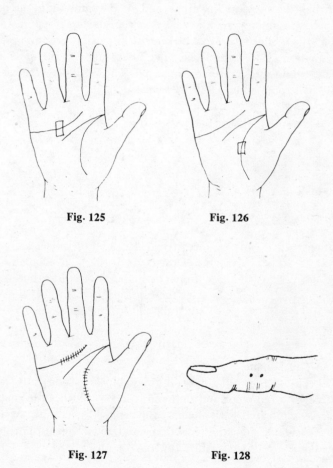

Fig. 125

Fig. 126

Fig. 127

Fig. 128

The Nail

Patients of pulmonary tuberculosis often wear convex nails, whose central parts are distinctly prominent and higher than the surrounding areas, and, at the same time, the nail tip bends downward like a shell or an inverted spoon (see Fig. 129). Slight sags can be seen on the nails through an examination against the light. The lower flaps of the nails are pale, while the semilunar flaps, pinkish. With a severe case, the nail roots show a purple hue.

Fig. 129

The Tongue

The tongue of a case of tuberculosis is generally featured by a red color and thin and pale fur. With a prolonged case complicated with anemia, the tongue looks pink. When the patient's digestive function is affected by antiphthisic medicine, yellowish white fur may be observed.

The Lip

A relatively large area of light-brown colored plaque

can be seen in the tunica intima of the upper lip.

The Eye

The patient of pulmonary tuberculosis is often characterized by pale and bright conjunctivas and long eyelashes.

The Tooth

If on the gums there appear red lines or patches of red subcutaneous hemorrhage, this indicates the case of pulmonary tuberculosis is accompanied by Vc deficiency. Therefore, while taking antiphthisic medicine, the intake of Vc should be supplemented.

The Ear

The ears are usually wizened and lusterless. Desquamation may occur at the acupoint representing the lung. On the opposite side to this point on the back of the ear, a node as big as a grain of millet is palpable.

The Facial Expression

Most of such patients wear a long and narrow face with a short space between the two eyes and a thin and narrow chin (see Fig. 130). Those with respiratory somatotype and tuberculous physiognomy, in particular, are susceptible to pulmonary tuberculosis. A red face indicates retention of pathogenic heat in the lung. Redness in one side of the face shows blood stasis in the lung on that same side. A purple face indicates poor pulmonay circulation, and an extremely heavy purple color heralds the danger of life. Blood stasis in the lung makes a desirable living place for tubercle bacilli and this is apt to cause tuberculosis. Chilliness in the limbs signifies the worsening of the case, while a feeling of heat in the endings of the limbs signifies a favorable omen of the case. Turbid spots may be observed on the forehead of a case of pulmonary tuberculosis.

The Neck

Purple contour of thin varicose veins can be seen around

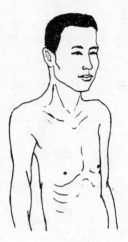

Fig. 130

the area between the 7th cervical vertebrae and the 3rd thoracic vertebrae.

The Physical Feature

A severe case of pulmonary tuberculosis may wear an extremely emaciated face, sunken eyeballs, glossy whites of the eyes, and long eyelashes. The face looks purple in color with reddish lips.

The Nose

The disease is often encountered among those who have a prominent nose with thin muscles.

Coronary Heart Diseases (Angina Pectoris and Myocardial Infarction)

Coronary heart diseases, alternately known as coronary atherosclerotic cardiopathy, are caused by myocardial ischemia and myocradial hypoxia resulting from coronary atherosclerosis. They are a most commonly encountered typical pathologic change caused by atherosis. Clinically, such diseases are generally symptomized as angina pectoris and myocardial infarction.

Angina Pectoris

This is a clinic syndrome of temporary ischema and hypoxia and is symptomized by paroxymal retrosternal pain or indisposition. It is the most common type of coronary heart diseases and belongs to, in the terminology of traditional Chinese medicine, the category of the obstruction of *qi* in the chest and angina pectoris.

1. Main Points for Diagnosis

a. In the retrosternal or the precardial area, there is a sudden and sharp coliky pain, which may radiate to the medial lateral of the left arm or the neck, often being accompanied, on the part of the patient, with a sense of oppression, depression or tightness. It is often induced by physical labor, emotional excitement (e. g. , anger, anxiety, etc.) or overeating.

b. The attack of the pain usually lasts for 3 to 5 minutes and usually not more than 15 minutes. The pain can be rapidly remitted by the patient himself after taking a rest or holding under his tongue nitroglycerin.

c. During the period of the attack of the pain by angina

pectoris, the patient's electrocardiogram indicates a displacement of the ST—T segment; with intermittent attacks, an exercise test on the electrocardiogram registers a positive reaction.

d. Such a disease occurs mostly in persons of 40 or above of age more often in men than in women.

2. Clinical Types

a. Angina Pectoris of the Stable Type

The nature of such type of angina pectoris usually remains unchanged within the period between 1 and 3 months, i. e. , the frequency of its attacks every day or every week is generally regular; the extent of fatigue and emotional excitement which causes the pain is similar; and the duration the attack of pain lasts for is much alike. That is why it is called typical angina pectoris.

b. Angina Pectoris of the Unstable Type

Such type of angina pectoris is characterized by: (1) the nature of the chest pain is changeable, its attacks are severer and its frenquency is greater; (2) the pain attacks when the patient is in tranquility and repose; (3) the pain attacks repeatedly and lasts each time for more than 15 or 20 minutes; (4) treatment with nitroglycerin becomes ineffective; (5) orginally there was no symptom but the initial attack began several weeks ago; (6) no distinct predisposing causes can be found; (7) change in the ST—T segment caused by ischemia is shown on ECG; and (8) no abnormal is discovered in zymology.

Myocardial Infarction

Myocardial infarction is the serious and lasting damage and necrosis of the myocardial ischemia type caused by the acute occlusion of the coronary artery. Mostly, such cases result from coronary sclerosis. It belongs to the most severe type among all the coronary heart diseases. In traditional

Chinese medicine, it belongs to the category of chest pain in the region of the glabella.

1. Main Points for Diagnosis

a. Several days or weeks before the heart attack, most patients had such fore-going symptoms as senses of acratia, indisposition in the chest, palpitation in activity, being short of breath and/or being restless, or has a typical case history of angina pectoris.

b. A sharp and persisting pain suddenly occurs in the retrosternal or the precardial area, and it cannot be remitted by taking a rest or by using nitroglycerin. It tends to be complicated with restlessness, sweating, fear or a sense of impending death.

c. It is often concomitant with such diseases as arrhythmia, heart failure or cardiogenic shock.

d. There is an increase in the WBC, an acceleration of the blood sendimentation and a rise in the serum creatine phosphokinase, in the GOT, the LDH and the urinary red protein, while the ECG shows characteristic abnormal waves, the elevation of the ST—T segment and the inversion of the T waves.

2. Methods of Diagnosis

The Color of the Palm

The palm looks red or dark red with dark red spots on the large thenar (see Fig. 131). There is the presence of a white cord prominence at the center of the root of the thumb, whose laterals bear the dark blue color and distinct blue contours of blood vessels (see Fig. 132).

The hand assumes the form of a square with short and thick fingers, which look drumstick-like or gecko-like (see Fig. 133). The palm is dropsical, the muscles are soft and lacks elasticity when pressed. Palpation shows the numbness of the sense and the inflexibility of the knuckles.

Fig. 131   Fig. 132

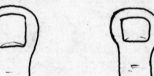

Fig. 133

138

The Palmar Line

a. There are "+"-shaped lines in the middle of Line 2, or there is the formation of "*"-shaped lines at the end of Line 2 (see Fig 134 and Fig 135)

Fig. 134   **Fig. 135**

b. There are insular lines or "□"-shaped lines at the upper part of Line 2 (see Fig. 136 and Fig. 137), which indicate the impending occurrence of myocardial infarction.

c. Line 3 bears insular lines at its end or it is intercepted by Line 6, which indicates the age of the patient when attacked by the disease (see Fig. 138 and Fig. 139).

d. Line 1 bears insular lines at the position close to the middle finger. This implies more clinical meaning for myocardial infarction (see Fig. 140)

e. Line 1 assumes a chain-like form with the possible presence of "*"-shaped lines at its part under the little finger (see Fig. 141).

The Nail

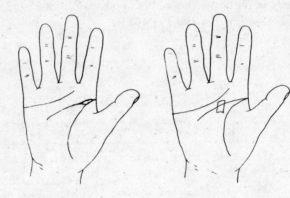

Fig. 136   Fig. 137

   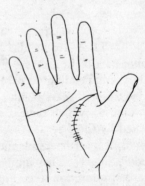

Fig. 138   Fig. 139

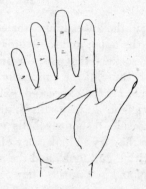
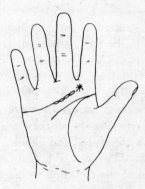

Fig. 140   Fig. 141

Square nails are often observed and especially the thumbs often wear square nails with vertical stripes. Meanwhile, in color and luster, the nails are checkered with red and white. The nails' beds close to the digital ends are much freshly redder than those at the middle, which are often pale and recover their color very slowly when pressed. With some cases, the root parts of the nails look seablue.

The Tongue

The tongue often has stasis of blood with ecchymosis and petechia. The texture of the tongue is usually purple, and a light color may be found if the duration of the illness has been long. The subligual vein is distinctly bulging.

The Lip

The color and luster of the tunica intima of the upper lip looks like cyanosis or is scarlet red, while the lips are cyanotic.

141

The Facial Expression

For most patients, the facial expression is pale or cyanotic, which will be worsened after fatigue or activity. With severe cases, the patient often looks puffy and wears an unpleasant expression. Besides that in the lower limbs, the edema in the face, especially that in the upper and lower lids, is distinct. The nerves at the eye sockets that control one's smiling may lose their functions because of the oppression of the edema so that a pleasant smile can be expressed. Such patients, even if they are truly joyous, can hardly smile a heartfelt smile on their faces. Besides, their eyeballs may look moistured and glossy. When they try to look, they often open their eyes wide and large with a dull look, and the motion of their eyelids seems clumsy and awkward. They often closely purse their lips and present wrinkles (mostly 3) between their eyebrows.

The acupuncture point named Jenchung often shows a dim blue color. The darkness of the acupuncture point named Yint'ang usually forecasts an unfavorable postdiagnosis.

The Ear

On the earlobes there may appear disordered foldings; the acupoint for the heart on the ear looks pale and is desquamative (see Fig. 142).

Hypertension

Hypertension, or primary hypertension, is chiefly characterized by the elevation of the blood pressure. Its pathologic cause has remained unknown. Based upon its clinical symptoms, traditional Chinese medicine has generally classified it into the category of vertigo and headache.

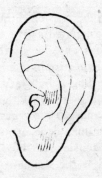

Fig. 142

1. Main Points for Diagnosis

a. One can be identified as a case of hypertension if his or her systolic pressure is as high as or higher than 21. 3 kPa. or his or her diastolic pressure is as high as or higher than 12. 5 kPa. , when either of which is confirmed by checking for twice. One whose diastolic pressure registers a height between 12 and 12. 5 kPa. can be identified as a case of critical hypertension.

b. When hypertension is determined, the type of symptomatic hypertension caused by various factors must be depleted before it can be diagnosed as a disease.

c. One can be diagnosed as a case of accelerated or malignant hypertension only if his or her case develops rapidly and vehemently, the diastolic pressure is continuously as high as or higher than 17. 3 kPa. and has bleeding or oozing of the fundus or the lorrhagia.

2. Clinical Types

a. Primary hypertension: the blood pressure has reached the height designated as the standard for hypertension and the case is free of any expressions of damages to the heart, the brain and the kidney.

b. Secondary hypertension: the blood pressure has reached the height designated as the standard for hypertension, and the case has any one of the following features: (1) left ventricular hypertrophy confirmed through X-ray, EDG or ultrasonic cardiography examination; (2) general or partial narrowing of the artery of the fundus confirmed by fundus examination; and (3) a low-grade increase in the proteinuria and the creastinine concentration of the plasma.

c. Tertiary hypertension: the blood pressure has reached the height designated as the standard for hypertension, and the case has any one of the following features: (1) cerebral hemorrhage or hypertensive encephalopathy; (2) left heart failure; (3) failure of the function of the kidney; (4) bleeding and oozing of blood of the fundus and papilledema.

3. Methods of Diagnosis

The Color of the Palm

The palm looks scarlet red, fat, thick and muscular with all the mounts being prominent. The appearance of such a palm often indicates, symultaneously, hyperlipemia.

A case of hypertension, whose palm is scarlet red, especially the large and the small thenar and the middle finger look scarlet red and is not fat and thick, is often complicated symultaneously with cardiac arrhythmias.

The palmar line

a. Under the ring finger, there are two parallel short lines running through Line 1 (see Fig. 143)

b. In the area designated as *Li*, the lines are scattered and disordered with the presence of " * " -shaped lines (see

144

Fig. 144).

Fig. 143   **Fig. 144**

c. The trend of Line 2 is level and straight, and the line is deep (see Fig. 145).

d. When there are " * " -shaped lines in the designated area named *Qian* in coordination with the " * " -shaped lines in the designated area named *Li*, a possible cerebrovascular accident must be guarded against. (see Fig. 146)

Fig. 145   **Fig. 146**

e. The presence of stellate lines at the acupuncture point named Pingyuan near the area designated as *Dui* indicates the possible occurrence of hemiparalysis during the period between 50 and 60 of one's age, but the conditions will be fine after recovery (see Fig. 147).

Fig. 147

The Nail

Mostly, the nails look short, especially those of both thumbs look flat and wide (see Fig. 148). The thumbs are usually short and stuff. The semilunar flaps of most hypertension cases look flat and large so much so that they reach or go beyond 1/3 of each of the nails.

The Tongue

The texture of the tongue looks dark purple, and usually there is yellow sticky fur at its root. However, after using medicine and maintaining the stability of the blood pressure, there may be white thin fur.

The sublingual vein is bulging distinctly with telangiectasis and looks blue-purple in color.

There is the filariform distribution of capillaries in the medial mucosa of the upper lip. Most smokers may show brownish apolocia sediments on the mucosa of the alveolar part.

The Facial Expression

The puffiness of the left lower lid indicates left ventricular hypertrophy, while the puffiness of the lower lids on both sides shows a severe case, which is often featured by cardiectasis, conjuctival congestion and the sense of interference and itching in the eye. With severe cases, bleeding of the fundus and papilledema of the optic nerve may be discovered. For patients of hypertension, when their eyeballs take an inward oblique direction in looking automatically, this expression often serves as a warning of an impending cerebral hemorrhage. The stasis of blood of the capillaries on the iris often indicates the existence of hypertension and arteriosclerosis.

The presence of wrinkles at the center of one's forehead with one vertical line at the acupuncture point named Yin-t'ang usually indicates the elevation of one's blood pressure. The presence of dark purple spots on the forehead indicates the existence of hypertension and a severe case which is difficult to cure. Such cases of hypertension are often complicated with constipation.

The Ear

The earlobes are mostly round and large and bear traces of horizontal interception (see Fig. 149).

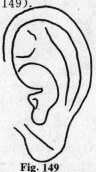

Fig. 148   **Fig. 149**

The Neck

The carotid pulsation of hypertension cases is usually vigorous, and, when looked in a side view, its pulsation can be observed.

Chronic Pulmonary Heart Disease

Chronic pulmonary heart disease is a kind of heart disease caused by the increase in the obstruction of the pulmonary circulation resulting from chronic pathologic changes in the lungs, the thorax or the pulmonary artery. The obstruction of the pulmonary circulation first gives rise to right ventricular hypertrophy and finally leads to right heart failure. The most common pathologic causes of pulmonary heart disease in China are chronic branchitis and obstructive emphysema, which constitue about 80% to 90% of all such cases. In traditional Chinese medicine, this disease belongs to the category of palpitation and asthma, cough and phlem retention, and watery distention.

1. Main Points for Diagnosis

a. The Stage of Pneumocardial Compensation:

When the compensatory function of the heart is relatively fine and the function of the lungs remains in the phase of partial compensation, the case, after some activities, may feel palmic, short of breath and hypodynamic, and a physical examination will readily register obvious pulmonary emphysema, pulmonary hypertension (the hyperfunction of the pulmonic second sound) and right ventricular dilatation (the presence of the systolic murmur in the tricuspid area and cardiac systolic beat under the xiphoid process).

b. The Stage of Pneumocardial Decompensation:

(1) Right Heart Failure: it is featured by the patient's

148

palpitation, acceleration of the heart rhythm, difficulty in breathing and the worsening of the cyanosis. A physical examination will show the obvious distention of the jugular vein, hepatomegaly with tenderness, positive reaction of hepalojugular reflux, obvious edema in the lower limbs, with possible presence of ascites, notable elevation of the venous pressure and the prolongation of its circulation.

(2) Respiratory Failure: it can be caused by two kinds of diseases. One is hypoxemia, which is characterized by retarted reaction, delirium, convulsion and coma caused by cyanosis, respiratory difficulty, acceleration of the heart rhythm and disorder of the brain function. The other is pneumocardial encephalopathy (hypoxemia and hypercapnia), which is a clinic syndrome characterized chiefly by disturbances of the nervous system appearing in the severe stage in the development of the respiratory failure. Symptoms of the nervous system may show disorder of consciousness such as lethargy and trance; mental symptoms may show excitation and restlessness; and nervous symptoms may show tremor, shiver and coma. Among symptoms of the eye, most common are conjestion of the bulba conjunctiva and chemosis. Other symptoms include peripheral angiectasis, filling of the superficial vein, warmth, hectic red and sweating of the skin and vigorousness of the pulse.

2. Methods of Diagnosis

The Color and Form of the Palm

a. Generally, the palm of the patient appears as a square with distinct edges and corners. The fingers of patients in an advanced stage are drumstick-like (see Fig. 150).

b. The palm looks purple-red in color with the presence of purple-blue color at the tips of all the fingers.

c. The contours of the blood vessels in the hand are distinct, especially the blue-purple contours of the blood vessels can easily be seen on the laterals and the middle segments of the fingers.

d. The muscles of the hand are prominent, but are soft and hypodynamic.

The Palmar Lines

a. Line 1 is intercepted with "川"-shaped lines (see Fig. 151).

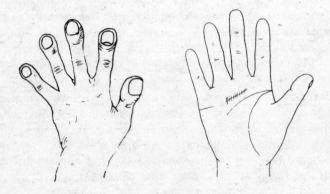

Fig. 150   **Fig. 151**

b. There are deep "+"-shaped lines and insular lines on Line 2 (see Fig. 152 and Fig. 153).

c. Line 3 is cut through by Line 6 and has, at its middle section, a rectangular frame (see Fig. 154 and Fig. 155).

d. There are " * "-shaped lines under the middle fingers (see Fig. 156).

e. There are horizontal lines or " # "-shaped lines in the designated areas named respectively *Qian* and *Dui* (see Fig.

Fig. 152

Fig. 153

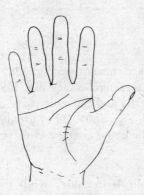

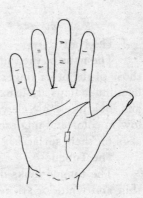

Fig. 154

Fig. 155

156).

   f. Possibly, there is on Line 4 the existence of insular
lines (see Fig. 157).

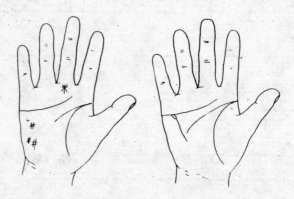

Fig. 156   **Fig. 157**

The Nail

The nails of the thumbs are square (see Fig. 158), while
those of the other fingers are rectangular (see Fig. 159). The
hemilunar flaps are usually high, and the nails curve upward
and look like eagle-claws (see Fig. 160). They are dark yellow in color and unglazed, thick and coarse, with ridges or
sags on their surfaces.

The Tongue

The tongue looks dark purple in color, while its fur is
thin and white or sticky and yellow. A tongue with sticky
and yellow fur indicates the existence of infection in the
lung.

   The sublingual vein bulges prominently and looks dark
purple in color like an earthworm coiling in a mass. Small

Fig. 158

Fig. 159

Fig. 160

153

veins are branching out like twigs of a tree from the main vein and extend to the outer laterals of the tongue. Their scarlet red color suggests a stable case, while the purple darkness of the small veins or the existence of hemorrhagic spots suggests a critical and severe case.

Rheumatic Fever

Rheumatic fever, a general alergic desmosis, chiefly offends the heart and the joints and often takes place with children and young adults. If not prevented and treated in time, it may result in rheumatic valvular disease of the heart. In traditional Chinese medicine, this disease is regarded as being of the category of arthralgia syndrome and obstruction of the heart-*qi*.

1. Main Points for Diagnosis

a. General syptoms: there is usually a case history of acute tonsillitis or pharyngitis which took place during the period between 1 and 4 weeks before the onset of this disease. It shows such symptoms as fever, sweat, fatigue and anorecticness. Or, the case has a history of rheumatic fever or rheumatic heart disease.

b. Myocarditis: clinic symptoms depend upon the seriousness and scope of the case, and commonly seen features include: (1) sinus tachycardia, disproportion of the heart rate to the temperature, quick heart rate even in sleeping or rest; (2) cardiac dilatation, and weak heart beat; (3) dull murmuring of the apex first sound like that of a fetal heart or that of the pendulum of a clock; with a severe case, possible presence of diastolic gallop rhythm; (4) frequent presence of systolic wind-blowing murmur above Grade II in the apical region of the heart and the aortic area, and sometimes the presence of a short and light diastolic murmur in the apical region of the heart; (5) a frequent arrhythmia, premature beat and atrioventricular block of Grade I, abnormal of the ST—T segment and the prolongation of the intervals of the Q—T waves on ECG; and (6) with severe cases, possible pericarditis or cardiac insufficiency.

c. Arthritis: most attacks occur on the main joints of the limbs with such features as being multiple, symmetrical and wandering; possible red swellings and heating pains in the acute stage without the possibility of resulting in joint deformation.

d. Pathologic changes in the skin: a few cases may show ringlike red spots, nodular red spots or subcutaneous nodule.

e. Chorea: often with female children.

2. Methods of Dignosis

The Color and Luster of the Palm

The palm of a case of rheumatic fever has a gloosy surface with fine, smooth and red skin. With some of such cases, distinct blue contours of the blood vessels can be observed in their palms which look blue mixed with purple in color.

There is an area discolor in the part of the large thenar near the root of the thumb (see Fig. 161).

The Palmar Lines

a. The presence of " + "-shaped lines or insular lines on Line 2 indicates that rheumatism has invaded the cardiovascular system. The case is often complicated with pathologic changes in the left ventricle (see Fig. 162 and Fig. 163).

b. The presence of relatively large branches at the ending section of Line 3 which extend toward the designated area *Qian* indicates that the joints have been invaded by the disease (see Fig. 164).

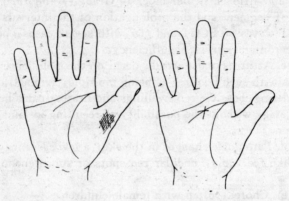

Fig. 161   Fig. 162

Fig. 163   Fig. 164

The Nail

The nails are husk-like with unglazed surfaces and both sides of their remote ends have become thickened and fragile. They look wizened, withered and yellow like rotten wood in color and sagging or broken in form with uneven surfaces. Such an appearance indicates the irregulation of the function of the circulatory system and the malnutrition of the finger tips because of the invasion of rheumatism (see Fig. 165).

Fig. 165

The Tongue

With an acute case of rheumatic disease, the tongue looks red, while with a long duration of illness, it looks purple or lusterlessly pale. A small tongue can be usually discovered.

With a case of rheumatic heart disease, the sublingual veins are mostly sticking out distinctly.

The Facial Expression

The face looks moistly red with the cheekbone areas being particularly scarlet. After a long duration of illness, a patient of rheumatic disease usually develops a wry nose bridge, the inclination of which may be employed to judge which side of the body is more seriously invaded by the disease. For instance, if the nose bridge inclines to the left, the pain in the joints of the left half of the body is more acute, while if it to the right, that in those of the right half of the body accordingly. The unevenness of the nose bridge suggests that the disease has invaded the spine.

The Ear

In the vertibral region of the auricle of such patients, projections can be palpated and such projections show tenderness.

The Eye

The left lower lids of such a case looks slightly blue in color with puffiness, and usually such a sign can be regarded as an omen of the invasion of rheumatism into the heart. And the case is often complicated with symultaneous pathologic changes caused by rheumatism in the cardiac valves.

The Physical Form

One who has a physical build of the muscular type is apt to contract rheumatism. The face of such a person is often "田" -shaped, and all the facial parts are well-proportioned. If we drew two parallel lines respectively below the eyebrows and the edge of the nose and thus divided the face into the upper, middle and lower sections, then, the vertical areas of these three sections would be almost the same. So it often looks like a square. The nose is not so prominent, the chin not so pointed either, but the forehead is high and broad. As a whole, the body is symmetric with long limbs. The muscles and the bones are both well developed.

Anemia

Anemia is a commonly encountered clinic syndrome. Factors which cause anemia are many, as its occurrence can be seen in many a case. Generally, the standards for the diagnosis of anemia are: for a male adult, his hemoglobin is less than 12 g. /dl or his erythrocyte is fewer than 4,000,000/mm^2; for a female adult, her hemoglobin is less than 10.5 g. /dl or her erythrocyte is fewer than 3,500,000/mm^2. In traditional Chinese medicine, anemia belongs to the category of deficiency of blood, consumative disease and blood depletion.

1. Clinic Types

Based upon its pathogenic factors, anemia may be divided into the following types:

a. Anerythropoiesis (or, anemia of defective blood formation)

(1) Deficits of substances or iron for the formation of blood, which may cause iron-defiency anemia; DNA synthesis obstruction resulting form deficits of folic acid or vitamin B_{12}, which cause megaloblastic anemia; and the weakening of the protoporphyrin synthesis resulting from the abnormal diabolism of vitamin B_6, which may cause vitamin B_6 reactive anemia. Besides, deficits of vitamin B_2, vitamin C and vitamin E or deficits of nicotinic acid, copper, protein and erythropoietin, all of which may cause anemia.

(2) Hemopoietic disorder: defection of the blood formation of the bone marrow, which may cause aplastic anemia, myelopathic anemia and various kinds of anemia resulting from some chronic diseases such as infection, hepatorenal diseases, rheumatoid arthritis and other demosis.

b. Excessive hemocytocatheresis: the defects of the red blood cells themselves and some external factors or the coexistence of both factors, which may cause hereditary anemia or acquired hemolytic anemia.

c. Blood loss: such as acute posthemorrhagic anemia and chronic posthemorrhagic anemia (or, iron-deficiency anemia).

Based upon its forms in accordance with the mean corpuscular volume (MCV), the mean corpuscular hemoglobin (MCH), and the mean corpuscular hemoglobin concentration (MCHC), anemia can be divided into four types:

a. Macrocytic anemia: it is featured by $MCV > 95\mu^2$, $MCH > 32\mu\mu g$, $MCH = 28$ to $32\mu\mu g$. and $MCHC = 31$ to 35 g./dl, and is encountered in such cases as megaloblastic anemia and normoblastic macrocytic anemia, such as hemolytic anemia and other kinds of anemia induced by liver and internal secretion diseases.

b. Normocytic anemia: it is featured by MCV = 82 to $95\mu^2$, and MCHC = 31 to 35 g. /dl, and is encountered in such cases as acute hemorrhagic anemia, some cases of hemolytic anemia, aplastic anemia and myelopathic anemia.

c. Microcytic normochromic anemia: it is featured by MCV < $82\mu^2$, MCH < $28\mu\mu$g. and MCHC = 31 g. /dl, and is encountered in such cases as subacute or chronic inflammatory diseases.

d. Microcytic hypochromic anemia: it is featured by MCV < $80\mu^2$, MCH < $28\mu\mu$g. and MCHC = 31g/dl, and is encountered in such cases as iron-deficiency anemia, maritime anemia and sideroblastic anemia.

e. The grading of anemia:

(1) Low-grade: hemoglobin registers 12 to 9. 1 g/dl;

(2) Moderate-grade: hemoglobin registers 9 to 6. 1 g/dl;

(3) Severe-grade: hemoglobin registers less than 6 g/dl.

2. Chief Symptoms

a. Acute Anemia: (1) acute loss of blood is chiefly symptomized as peripheral circulatory failure, fall of blood pressure and shock; large quantity but low-speed loss of blood may result in such symptoms as dizziness, thirst, hypodynamia, rapid and weak pulse and faint; (2) acute hemolysis is chiefly symptomized as fever, blood deficiency, jaundice, pain in the waist, nemoglobinuria and splenomegaly.

b. Chronic Anemia: it is chiefly symptomized as headache, dizziness, tinnitus, dim eyesight (always with a black spot in the vision), intolerance of cold, hypodynamia and fatigue, sleeplessness, anorexia, nausea, vomiting, abdominal distention, dyspepsia, glossitis, mucocutaneous paleness, cardio plamus and shortness of breath; with severe cases, there may be puffiness, cardiectasis and systolic murmur in the apical region of the heart.

3. Methods of Diagnosis

The Color and Luster of the Palm

The palm looks pale and has a lower temperature than both the large and the small thenar, which present a sag after being pressed and are slow in recovering their normal states. The lines and stripes at the foldings of the palm look pale, bloodless and lusterless; the fingers are mostly cold and taper-like with thin and long tips. In the palm there can be seen dim blue contours of the blood vessels, which extend toward the roots of the fingers, and in the designated area named *Gen*, there is a blue-pale mass (see Fig. 166). In its form, the palm bends toward the little finger with the thumb as the center.

The Palmar Lines

There are unneatly-distributed and relatively shallow "+"-shaped lines in the area of Line 2, on which there also may be insular lines (see Fig. 167). Besides there are Lines

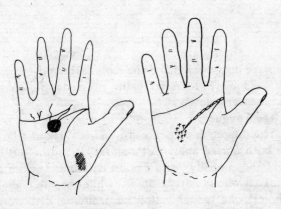

Fig. 166   Fig. 167

6 cutting through Line 3, which is often shallow and short with possible branches or is chain-like (see Fig. 168). At its ending part there are often large insular lines.

The Nail

The nails are pale in color and are mostly small nails (see Fig. 169)with pointed tips(see Fig. 170). The semilunar

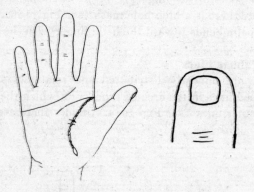

Fig. 168   Fig. 169

flaps have disappeared and the nails assume the form of a ladle (see Fig. 171). After being pressed, the color of the blood recovers slowly.

The Tongue

The tongue is pale in color and is thick and large in its form with dotted spots in its sides. It can be put out very slowly and clumsily, and has on it thin and white fur. the sublingual vein is fairly colored, while the sublingual part as a whole looks tender yellow or white as if it were coated with a membrance.

Fig. 170   Fig. 171

The Lip
The tunica intima of the upper lip is lighter in color than the tongue. Both lips look pale and even a white rim is formed along their edges (see Fig. 172).

The Facial Expression
The area in the vicinity of the acupoint named Jenchung is short and shallow and appears ladder-shaped. With a severe case, the area is even and flat and is almost invisible (see Fig. 173).

Patients of anemia mostly have thin and pointed chins, which are quite disproportionate to the upper and lower sections of the face. With a case of chronic anemia, the whole face is generally large and wide with the lower section being even broader and the chin being sharply pointed. There is usually a broad space between the two pupils of the eyes and a short distance between the nose root and the upper lip. His

Fig. 172

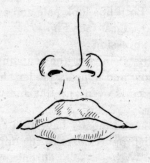

Fig. 173

164

or her facial color is blue or pale. Most of such cases wear an ill-looking complexion (see Fig. 174), with droopings below

Fig. 174

the eyes. With some cases of anemia, such as those of aplastic anemia and iron-deficiency anemia, their skin looks blue-purple like the color of a muskmelon, or the texture of their skin looks like silk. Besides, many hemorrhagic spots may be observed in the uncovered parts of their bodies.

The Nose

The nose looks pale, while its edges look tender yellow.

The Eye

The conjunctiva looks pale. With children, it becomes blue-green, which is usually caused by iron deficiency.

The Ear

The ear, after being rubbed, recovers its blood color slowly.

The Hair

Cases of anemia are subject to the loss of hairs, even

suffer from baldness (resulting in a bald head), and are characterized by the thickness of individual hairs.

The Physical Form

Patients of anemia have glossy skin in the lower limbs below the knee joints, and the hairs on the skin of the legs are apt to fall due to the weakness of the roots of the hairs. Generally, the trunk of such a case is more developed than the limbs and the muscles are soft.

Chronic Gastritis

The disease chronic gastritis refers to various chronic endogastric pathologic changes caused by different pathogenic factors. In the diagnostics of traditional Chinese medicine, it is put into the category of epigastragia, acid regurgitation and gastric discomfort with acid regurgitation.

1. Main Points for Diagnosis

This disease manifests long-term, various-formed symptoms of the digestive tract, such as pain in the upper abdominal part, satiety, heartburn, different-degree dyspepsia. Atrophic gastritis may be symptomized as anarexia, leanness, anemia, glossitis and lingual papilla atrophy.

a. Superficial Gastritis: it is mostly distinctly manifested in the antral region of the stomach, usually of the defuse type. The surface of the gastric mucosa often presents red-and-white-checkered or piebaldistic changes. Sometimes, there exists scattered erosion, and often with greyish or yellow exudate. These symptoms may be localized reaction.

b. Atrophi Gastritis: usually, the mucous membrane looks pale or greyish, and the plica has become finer or flatter, while the submucous blood vessels look through fluoroscopy purple-blue in color. But the color of the mucosa generally depends on such factors as the level of the hemoglobin. The pathologic change may either be of the defuse type or occur chiefly in the antral region of the stomach.

2. Methods of Diagnosis

The Color and Luster of the Palm

The color of the palm of such a case is often mixed with blue and yellow, the designated area named *Zhen* looks apparently tender yellow and is spongy and sagging, while the area designated as *Gen* looks blue-pale with flaccid muscles. With a complicated case of gastroptosia, the fingers are distinctly longer than the palm itself (i. e. , the distance between the root of the middle finger and its tip is greater than that between the root of the wrist and the root of the middle finger). For some cases, when they put together all their five fingers, the hand as a whole looks like the bone of a cuttlefish; both laterals of the large and the small thenar are invisible along the lateral of the palm; the skin often looks pale; there are quite a number of thin and fragmentary lines on the palm; and the palm itself appears trangular and is not forceful. Such a palm is known as a "cuttlefish-bone-shaped" palm (see Fig. 175). Besides, for some other cases, when they put together all their 10 fingers there are large crevices between the roots of the fingers which assume the form of a bamboo joint (see Fig. 176). Mostly, the fingers of such patients are thin and long, but often with square nails (see Fig. 177), particularly distinct with those of the index fingers.

The Palmar Line

a. There are "#"-shaped lines or "*"-shaped lines in the area designated as *Zhen*, which is sagging (see Fig. 178).

b. There are stripe-like lines or "#"-shaped lines in the

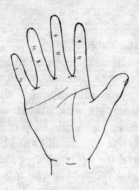

Fig. 175

Fig. 176

Fig. 177

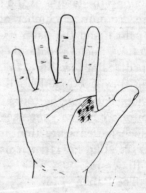

Fig. 178

area designated as *Gen* (see Fig. 179).

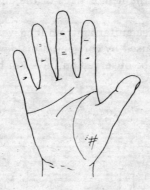

Fig. 179

c. On the left palm, there are disordered lines which mostly appear as "#"-shaped lines (see Fig. 180).

Fig. 180

d. When Line 4 is short and deep or disconnected and is homologous with the intercepting traces at the conjuctive position of the areas designated as *Zhen* and *Gen*, it suggests the trend toward the hemorrhage of the digestive track (see Fig. 181).

e. With a case suffering from long-year feeble function of the stomach caused by congenital maldevelopment, chain-shaped lines may be observed on Line 3 of his palm (see Fig. 182).

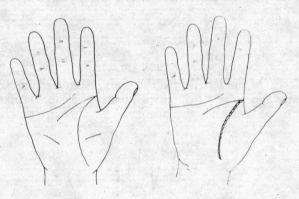

Fig. 181   Fig. 182

The Nail

The finger nails of a patient suffering from stomach troubles are usually crisp, fragile and lusterless, and may show dim white spots.

The Tongue

With a newly developed case, the tongue looks red with yellow or sticky fur, while with a case who has suffered long, the tongue is light in color with thin and white fur.

With a case of atrophic gastritis, the tongue is red with yellow fur, indicating a distinct inflammation and the existence of superfacial ulcer. A red tongue without fur and little saliva or with thin and white fur is a common feature of atrophic gastriris.

With a case of gastritis, if the sublingual small vein is not distinct and the sublingual vein is not varicose, it indicates the stability of the case, while if the sublingual small vein branches out from the sublingual vein like branches from the stem of a tree and extends toward the edges of the tongue, it indicates that the superfacial gastritis has developed into atrophic gastritis. The existence of large numbers of branches and the presence of small hemorrhagic spots or brownish old hemorrhagic spots at the endings suggest that the atrophic gastritis tends to be intestinalized. Furthermore, if the blood vessels seem to be coated with a white membrane, then, a possible case of carcinoma must be taken into consideration (see Fig. 183).

The Tooth

Generally, patients of gastritis have relatively small teeth with red swollen dental alveoli. They are subject to gingival hemorrhage.

The Ear

At the acupoint for the stomach on the left ear, chondral hyperplasis can be palpable; and the inclination of the prominence toward the lateral of the face mostly suggests a case of gastritis. Moreover, the duration of illness of such a case may be judged in accor-

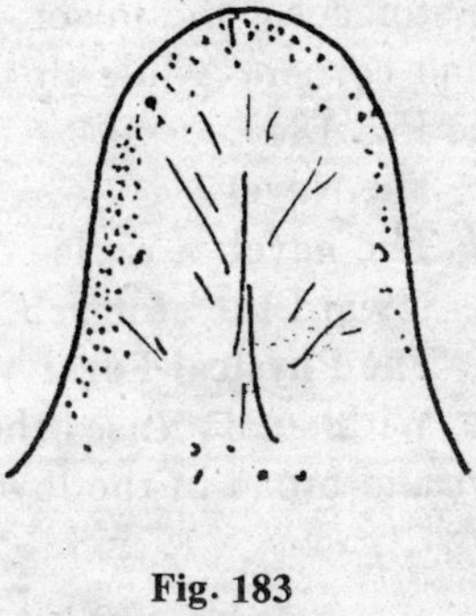

Fig. 183

171

dance with the size of the prominence. The existence of such a prominence generally suggests a duration of illness between 3 and 5 years; if the prominence is as big as half a mung bean, it indicates that the duration may have lasted for about 10 years; and if its size is larger than that of half a mung bean, then , it indicates that the duration is more than 10 years now.

The Eye

With a case of gastritis, the pupils of the two eyes tend to be relatively small, and the eyeballs automatically take an outward oblique vision.

The Facial Expression

The complexion is usually yellow, and especially the periphery of the mouth and lips and the vicinity of the nose bridge bear the color of loess. Often, there is a very short distance between the two eyes which are hollow usually. When the stomach with chronic gastritis becomes acute, the patient's upper lip will become blue, and the acupoint Yin-t′ang looks blue, too. With one who has a feeble function of the stomach, the lower jaw usually assumes the form of a round corner, while th face often appears as a "申" shape (see Fig. 184).

The Navel

The navel of a case of gastritis is round-shaped, and it tilts toward the stomach.

The Physical Form

With such a case, the body is often narrow in the upper part and broad in the lower.

Peptic Ulcer

The term peptic ulcer refers to the chronic ulcer in the digestive canal resulting from its contact with the gastric

172

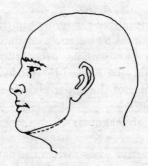

Fig. 184

juice which contains acid and pepsase. As it is encountered in
the stomach and the duodenum, it is alternately known as
gastroduodenal ulcer. Based on its clinic symptoms, traditional Chinese medicine includes it in the category of epigas-
tralgia, epigastric pain and gastri discomfort with acid regurgitation.

1. Main Points for Diagnosis

a. The aching in the upper abdomen occurs chronically
and periodically. It can be worsened by such factors as sea-
sonal changes (the end of fall, winter and spring), fatigue
and irregular diet, but it can be remitted after a rest or taking alkaline drugs.

b. The aching is generally featured by its regularity.
The ache caused by gastric ulcer mostly occurs during the
period of time between half an hour and 2 hours after meal
and will be automatically remitted after lasting for one or
two hours. So it follows a rule of eating → aching → remit-

ting. The ache caused by duodenal ulcer usually occurs in 3 or 4 hours after meal and will not be remitted until the next meal time. So it follows a rule of aching → eating → remitting. Such patients are often awakened at night by the aching.

c. There is a localized tenderness in the upper abdomen. The tenderness caused by gastric ulcer mostly exists right at the center under the xiphoid process or at the position slightly left, while that caused by duodenal ulcer is usually located at the center of the upper abdomen or at the position slightly upper left.

2. Methods of Diagnosis

The Hand

a. With ulcerative cases, when the patient puts together all his or her fingers, there are relatively large gaps between the fingers.

b. The central area of the palm looks dark-blue (see Fig. 185).

c. The palm itself registers a fall of the temperature.

d. The area designated as *Zhen* is soft and hollow (see again Fig. 185).

e. With a case of duodenal ulcer, the length of the palm surface is greater than that from the root of the middle finger to its tip (see Fig. 186). With one whose fingers are noticeably short and thick, a possible case of duodenal ulcer should be taken into particular consideration.

The Palmar Line

a. With an ulcerative case, in the area designated as *Zhen* on the palm, "#"-shaped lines may be observed and there is a relatively deep line which divides the areas designated as *Zhen* and *Gen* on the palm. The deeper this line is, the greater the possibility is that a possible hemorrhage of the ulcer of the digestive canal occurs (see Fig. 187).

174

b. Line 3 appears in a chain shape (see Fig. 188).

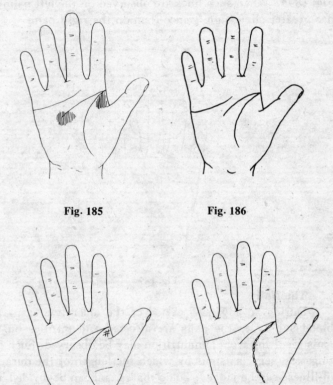

Fig. 185

Fig. 186

Fig. 187

Fig. 188

175

c. With most of such cases, Line 1 is relatively long, so long so that it reaches the area designated as *Xun* (see Fig. 189). When such lines are observed on the left palm, it has greater clinic significance than on the right palm.

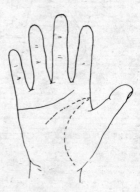

Fig. 189

The Nail

During an advanced period of the ulcerative case, the blood supply to the nails are affected and pittings on the nails resulting from lamnutrition may be observed. Such pittings can serve as signs by which the length of the duration of illness can be judged. To do that, a nail can be divided into 5 sections respectively representing 5 months. If the pittings are present at the middle section, then, it will indicate that the case was severer three months ago (see Fig. 190). Meanwhile, the nails usually do not have semilunar flaps or appear as small nails, with the index finger looking particularly small (see Fig. 191). Gencrally, there are vertical stripes on the nail of the thumb (see Fig. 192). With year-long and prolonged cases, the nails are usually flat and level or cocked up (see Fig. 193).

Fig. 190

Fig. 191

Fig. 192

Fig. 193

The Tongue

With most cases of duodenal ulcer, the tongue is light in color with thin and white fur, while with those of gastric ulcer, the tongue looks red with yellow fur.

The Lip

With a case whose ulcer exists in the great curvature of the stomach, common is the symultaneous presence of ulcer in the left corners of the lips, in the mucosa of the left cheek or in that of the left lateral of the tongue. With a case whose ulcer occurs in the small curvature of the stomach, common is the symultaneous presence of ulcer in the right corner of the lips, in the mucosa of the right cheek or in the right lateral of the tongue (see Fig. 194).

The Tooth

Ulcerative cases of the digestive canal usually show unevenly-arranged teeth and are apt to contract inflammation in the gums featured by red swelling, the sense of soreness and aching and loose teeth.

At the point on the back of the ear homologous to the acupoint for the stomach on the ear, a small hyperplastic object like a grain of millet in size may be palpable. In diagnosing, its presence in the left ear is more meaningful than that in the right ear. If such an object presents itself on both ears, the case can be definitely identified as gastric ulcer. At the point on the back of the ear homologous to the acupoint for the duodenum, the presence of a hyperplastic object like a grain of millet in size can be identified as a case of duodenal ulcer.

The Facial Expression

Mostly, such cases wear an ulcerative complexion, which is also known as the internal-organ-pendulous complexion. It is characterized by a proper distance between the two pupils and noticeable hollow eyeholes. With a case of gastric ulcer, the voice is low and feeble, the fingers are long with hollow nails, while with a case of duodenal ulcer, the patient is usually hot-tempered, the fingers are short and thick with broad nails free of semilunar flaps (see Fig. 195). Mostly, the face looks pale or yellow mixed with white

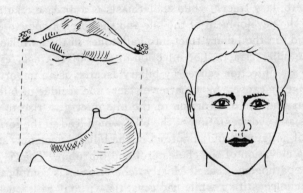

Fig. 194   Fig. 195

and lusterless. The nose and the acupoint named Yint'ang of such a case look dark, and their distinct blue color may show the acuteness of the aching.

The Physical Form

One who often shows the following postures is apt to develop gastric ulcer: a protruding lower jaw, a hunchback, round but askew shoulders, a bulging abdomen, frequently putting the left hand on the back, pressing the abdomen with the right hand, and constantly turning the body to the left side.

The spine of such a case is not neat and level, often with bumps and sags.

With a case of gastric ulcer, there is the occurence of the paraluxation of the fifth thoratic vertebrae, and there is tenderness in that area.

Cholecystitis and Cholelithiasis

Cholecystitis is the inflammation caused by the infection of the biliary tract, while cholethiasis is a disease resulting from the development of the bile and the foreign body (e. g. , ascarid) in the biliary tract into gallstones in the gallbladder or the biliary tract. The infection of the biliary tract, especially the infection caused by biliary ascaris, is an important pathogenic cause. As a matter of fact, the sesidue of biliary ascaris and the obstruction of the bile duct give rise to the stasis and sedimentation of the bile, which lead to the formation of gallstones and abnormal of the biliary elements, such as the elevation of the cholesterol and bilirubin. That is the major pathogenic cause. Mostly, cholethiasis is complicated with cholecystitis, while cholecystitis without gallstones is rare. The infection of the biliary tract may induce lithogenesis, while gallstones, in their turn, may also induce the infection of the biliary tract. Therefore, these two diseases are closely related. Cholecystitis and cholelithiasis are often encountered among middle-aged and elderly people who have fatty constitutions, and more often with men than with women. So far, such diseases have become commonly seen in China, as the number of such cases has been increasing with every passing day. In the terminology of traditional Chinese medicine, they are known as "accumulation of pathogens in the chest. "

1. Main Points for Diagnosis

   a. Acute cholecystitis is chiefly symptomized as an

abrupt pain in the right upper abdomen, fever, chilliness, nausea, vomiting, and, with some cases, the presence of jaundice. The pain in the upper abdomen is colicky and in radiation to the shoulder-back area, resulting in a reflexion deformity of the body. Elderly patients are subject to biliary necrosis and perforation, and are apt to manifest symptoms of shock. Therefore, a sharp vigilance must be constantly maintained.

b. The symptoms of a case of chronic cholecysis is generally indistinct. A typical case often shows some clinic symptoms of acute cholecystitis such as biliary colic, fever, etc. An atypical case chiefly manifests such gastro-intestinal symptoms as an irregular pain in the upper abdomen, abdominal distention, constipation, indigestion, bad appetite for fatty food, nausea and hiccup. Usually, the patient has a sense of indigestion of fried and greasy food.

c. Cholelithiasis often occurs among fat middle-aged women. It has been reported that of all the women of 60 and above of age, one out of three has contracted cholelithiasis, while the rate of such disease incidences among the men, only about 1/8. Among elderly people, such rate is the highest, but about half of all the cases manifest indistinct symptoms.

2. Chief Symptoms

Cholelithiasis may repeatedly attack, and, with some cases, can last as long as decades.

Abdominal pain, fever and jaundice are the three most important symptoms during the acute stage. The abdominal pain expresses itself as a colic in the upper right abdomen, and in radiation to the shoulder-back area. With a severe case, the pain may make the patient turn over and over with cold sweat on the head, and when the abdominal pain attacks, it is often accompanied with such symptoms as nausea and vomiting. Generally, the jaundice is light and short, but if it is severe and lasts long, it suggests a complicated infection. Most symptoms manifested during the acute stage have apparent predisposing causes, most common of which include: excessive eating, drinking, fatigue, severe constipation resulting from eating too much greasy food, and excitation.

Every case of cholelithiasis does not necessarily show symptoms of the acute stage. Most cases show indistinct or no symptoms at all. Only when the gallstones have grown larger, have moved to the biliary duct and thus have led to its spasm, may such a case manifest the above-mentioned symptoms. After the acute stage (alternately known as the stage of attack), there is an intermission, in which, when there is no inflammation or after the extinction of the inflammation, the major symptoms manifested by the patient may be a distending pain and a disordered function of the gastro-intestinal tract.

3. Methods of Diagnosis

The Color and Luster of the Palm

The palm is plump and muscular with the prominence of all the mounts, which is particularly obvious in the areas designated as *Kun* and *Li*. The area designated as *Xun* looks crimson in color with red spots which are decolored when pressed. Especially, when the patient puts his or her palm with its surface upward, it can be observed that the ring finger is noticeably lean and weak (see Fig. 196).

The Palmar Lines

a. There is the presence of Line 6 on the middle section of Line 3, or the formation of insular lines there (see Fig. 197 and Fig. 198).

b. Line 4 is deep and short (see Fig. 199).

c. The area designated as *Gen* looks purple-blue in color (see Fig. 200).

d. The presence of " ∗. " -shaped, " # " -shaped or

"×" -shaped lines in the area designated as *Xun* (the presence in the area on the right palm means more)suggests possible weakening of the function of the gallbladder. Among the lines, the "×"-shaped ones indicate a slightest case; the "#" -shaped ones, a case of inflammation; and the " * " - shaped ones, a case of cholelithiasis. If all these lines are circumscribed with a square frame, then, it suggests a severe case of cholelithiasis which demands a surgical operation or indicates the formation of lines after an operative treatment (see Fig. 201, Fig. 202, Fig. 203, Fig. 204 and Fig. 205). The symultaneous existence of such lines and a lean and feeble ringfinger will mean a great deal more.

The Nail

The nails are mostly square in shape and small in size and most noticeable is the index finger (see Fig. 206). There are quite a number of vertical stripes on the thumb (see Fig. 207).

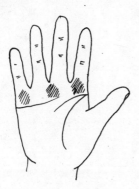

Fig. 196

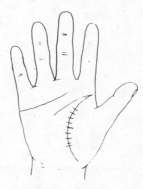

Fig. 197

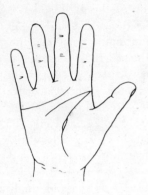

Fig. 198

Fig. 199

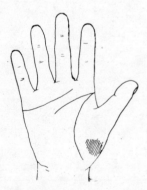

Fig. 200

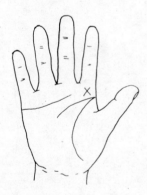

Fig. 201

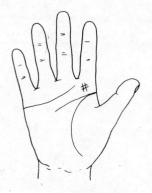

Fig. 202

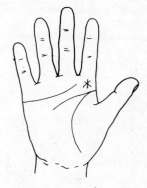

Fig. 203

Fig. 204

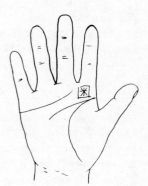

Fig. 205

Fig. 206   Fig. 207

The Tongue

The tongue looks pink with thin and white fur, and that can be identified as cholecystits; if the laterals of the tongue look scarlet with white or yellow sticky fur, it may be identified as cholelithiasis. Most meaningful is a tongue fully covered with yellow and sticky fur.

The subligual xanthochromia indicates stasis of the bile and it appears earlier than the sclera xanthochromia, but after some treatment the sclera xanthochromia disappears before the sublingual xanthochronmia does. With some cases, during the stationary phase of illness, the sublingual xanthochromia does not disappear.

The Ear

The emerging of small blood vessels at the acupoint for the gallbladder on the ear indicates the acute stage of cholecystitis. If a proliferative object as big as a grain of bean is observed in the soft tissues, it can be identified as chronic cholecystitis; and if a proliferative object as big as a grain of millet emerges at the homologous point on the back of the ear, it can be identified as the sign of cholelithiasis.

The Facial Expression

One whose function of the gallbladder is feeble usually wears a broad face, a round lower jaw and is amiable but grave in manner and honest in character. The face is round with a relatively narrow space between the two pupils and looks red and lustrous. One whose face looks red but mixed with dark purple is subject to cholelithiasis. Such a case is usually plump in his or her physical build with a neat and level spine. Most particular is the feature that the lower jaw of a patient of cholelithiasis appears as an obtuse triangle.

The Neck

One who has contracted cholecystitis usually has a plump and short neck. The presence of a vegetation as big as a grain of millet on the skin of the neck often has greater clinical significance.

The Physical Form

With such cases, there is tenderness in all the 4th, 5th and 9th thoratic vertebrae. One who has a feeble delative function of the gallbladder usually has keen tenderness in the 9th thoratic vertebrae, while one who has a weak contractibility of the gallbladder tends to have distinct tenderness in the 4th and 5th thoratic vertebrae.

Virus Hepatitis

Virus hepatitis is an infectious disease of the digestive tract caused by hepatitis virus. The degeneration and the necrosis of the liver cells and the inflammatory infiltration of the interstitial tissues of the liver are symptomatic of the pathologic changes. Due to the difference in the pathogens, hepatitis is divided into five types, i. e. , hepatitis A, B, C, D and E. In traditional Chinese medicine, it is generally categorized as jaundice, pain in the rib and fulminant jaundice.

1. Main Points for Diagnosis

a. The presence of symptoms which have been manifested consistently for several days in succession over a recent period and cannot be explained with other pathogenic factors, such as feeling exhausted, losing appetite, nausea, feeling disgusted with fatty food, abdominal distention, diarrhea, liver pain, brown urine, fever, etc.

b. Physical features: enlargement of the liver and tenderness; with some cases, slight enlargement of the spleen and the presence of jaundice.

c. Blood test: elevation of the SGPT, especially with a high numerical value (over 4 times higher than the normal) and a relatively long duration of the state. The positive reaction of the HBs Ag is conducive to the diagnosis of hepatitis B.

2. Clinical Types

a. Acute hepatitis

(1) acute anicteric hepatitis

(2) acute icterohepatitis

b. Chronic hepatitis

(1) chronic metastatic hepatitis

(2) chronic active hepatitis

(3) chronic hepatitis of the severe type (including severe chronic active hepatitis and cirrhosis of high activity)

c. Hepatitis of the severe type

(1) acute severe hepatitis (or fulminant hepatitis)

(2) subacute severe hepatitis (or subacute hepatic necro-

sis)

(3) cholestatic hepatitis

3. Methods of Diagnosis

The Color and Luster of the Palm

a. With such cases as of acute icterohepatitis, chronic active hepatitis of the severe type, chronic active hepatitis, active hepatitis of the severe type, subacute hepatitis of the severe type, and cholestatic hepatitis, the palm usually bears the color of dark yellow. A tender yellow and lustrous palm suggests a lighter case, while a gray-yellow or a turbid yellow palm, a severe case. The yellow color first appears in the areas designated as *Xun* and *Zhen* along Line 2, but if it develops and appears in the three areas designated as *Dui*, *Qian* and *Gen*, and, symultaneously, with scarlet red spots, then, it suggests a complicated case of the elevation of the transaminase. If the pulsing of the artery is palpable at the opposite side to the acupoint Hoku near the middle section of Line 2 in the area of "Yellow," it may be identified as a case of portal hypertension. If the scarlet red color shown in the areas designated as *Dui*, *Qian* and *Gen* becomes dark or gives out a hue of bluish paleness, it indicates the completion of the formation of chronic hepatitis or cirrhosis.

b. If the area designated as *Kun* at the root of the little finger is darkening and Line 1, Line 2 and Line 3 all bear the color of light brown, it generally indicates the existence of the infective period of virus hepatitis.

c. During the initial phase when the virus has invaded, the palm mostly looks dark and lusterless, and both the large and the small thenar become dark blue and prominent with a sore tenderness when pressed.

d. If the center of the palm is encircled with a hue of a dark blue color and the center itself is lightly colored, it generally indicates that the patient suffers from "the hyperactive liver-*qi* attacking the stomach" so that he or she bears such symptoms as a poor appetite, feeling disgusted with fatty food, etc.

e. If the first segment and the root of the little finger look lightly colored and lusterless and the very center of the palm and its area designated as *Kan* look pale and dry, it indicates the weakening of the general resistance of the bodily organs, which is chiefly symptomized as feeling exhausted. Such a case is often observed in a patient of chronic metastatic hepatitis.

f. The presence of pigmentation in the hand with black spots and uneven distribution or with vascular spiders is symptomatic of cirrhosis.

The Palmar Line

a. With a case of acute hepatitis, Line 4 is mostly shallow and lightly colored or is connected intermittently, while with a case of chronic hepatitis, it looks deep and long and has a "ノ\" -shaped line homologous with it horizontally and deeply intercepting between the areas desiganted as *Zhen* and *Gen*. Furthermore, the presence of a short and discolored Line 4 suggests an unfavorable prognosis, and, most likely, the case will develop into cirrhosis (see Fig. 208).

b. Line 3 is cut by interference lines (see Fig. 209).

c. The areas desiganted as *Zhen* and *Xun* are disordered with "#" -shaped and square-frame lines (see Fig. 210).

d. If Line 3 is broken halfway and its section near the center of the palm looks slightly pale with a hue of wizened yellow right under this section, and if the upper end of Line 3 and the outer lateral of the thumb look dark blue and haggard and are prominent and stiff in its texture when pressed, it indicates a case of hepatosplenomegaly (see Fig. 211). The formation of relatively long insular lines in the middle section of Line 3 on the left palm can be more reli-

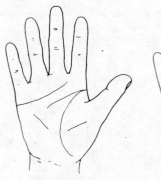

Fig. 208   Fig. 209

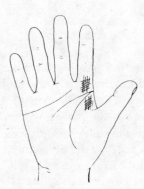

Fig. 210   Fig. 211

ably identified as splenomegaly (see Fiy. 212).

e. The area encircled by Line 1 is larger than that by Line 3 (see Fig. 213).

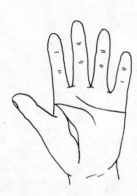

Fig. 212   **Fig. 213**

f. The fingers bend toward the thumb.

The Nail

The subungual color is pale, and there are prominences on the nail in the form of stringed pearls. The nails are ladle-shaped or soft and thin (see Fig. 214, Fig. 215 and Fig. 216). With a prolonged case, the nail matrix on both sides of the nail body bears a purple-blue and withered yellow color, and, possibly, there may be the presence of such nail features as blue, black, thick erosive scars.

The Tongue

With cases of acute hepatitis, during the initial phase, the texture of the tongue is red and the fur is white and sticky with the edges of the tongue being particulavly red. But when gastro-intestinal symptoms become more notice-

Fig. 214   Fig. 215

Fig. 216

able such as severe jaundice, vomiting and feeling disgusted with fatty food, the fur on the tongue will turn yellow and sticky. With cases of chronic hepatitis, generally, the fur is thin and obvious and changes have taken place in the texture of the tongue as it bears a dark purple color and gives out a hue of blue or green.

During the phase of cirrhosis which is often complicated with hepatic dysfunction confirmed through various tests, the tongue usually looks yellowish pale and sticky. However, more often than not, the tongue looks dry and red without any fur or looks dark purple like pork liver with little fur and saliva. This can be observed through specular reflexion.

During the phase of jaundice, the sublingual area and particularly the root part of the tongue bear a yellow color, which appears earlier than the iclera sclera does. Furthermore, the sublingual sclera begins to extinct only after the extinction of the iclera sclera. With a case of hepatosplenomegaly, the sublingual vein usually becomes purple and thick with stasis of blood.

During the phase of cirrhosis, the sublingual vein becomes twisted and cirsoid and is often complicated with sublingual capillarectasia.

The Lip

With a case of hepatitis, the intimal region of the upper lip is darkly colored, and there may be white granules like grains of millet in size on the labial frenum, which are usually caused by the varicose inferior vena cave and nevose sore. The possible presence of large pieces of brown macular patches in the intimal region of the upper lip forecasts an unfaverable recovery from the liver disease. The pale color and the lusterlessness of the intimal of the upper lip indicate a case of chronic hepatitis with a complication of anemia.

The Eye

194

During the acute stage, there is the presence of iris xanthochromia, while during the chronic stage, the iris is covered with blood strings. The eyes tend to look inward with large pupils, and sometimes a "—"-shaped blood vessel running horizontally across the eyeball may be observed. If it presents itself in the right eye, it suggests a case of liver disease, but if in the left eye, a case of stomach trouble. Such a feature is often encountered among great drinkers (see Fig. 217).

Fig. 217

The Ear

With a prolonged case of hepatitis, desquamation may be observed and cartilage proliferation may be palpated in the liver and spleen areas on the ear. If the proliferation is round and as big as a grain of mung bean, it indicates that the disease has already lasted for 5 to 10 years; if there are hard granules as big as grains of millet on the back of the ear, it usually forecasts an unfaverable prognosis as the disease tends to develop into cirrhosis or liver cancer. If the granules appear on both ears, then, it will mean a great deal more. Acute hepatitis can show the presence of blue capillaries in the areas on the ear respectively representing the liver and the abdominal cavity.

The Physical Form

a. With a case of hepatitis, the presence of cobweb-shaped capillaries on the cheeks usually indicates a case of alcoholic cirrhosis. The mandibular fossa (i. e. , the part under the lower lip and above the tip of the chin) usually looks gray or dark brown.

b. Cases of hepatitis are mostly complicated with pains in the joint of the right knee, in the ankle joint of the left foot and in the right foot.

c. Cases of hepatitis are often featured by accessory luxation in the 4th and 8th thoratic vertebrae, which, therefore, bear tenderness.

Portal Cirrhosis

Portal cirrhosis is a common type of cirrhosis and constitutes a percentage of about 50 among all the cases of cirrhosis. There are many pathogenic factors which cause portal cirrhosis, but the major ones are virus hepatitis, chronic alcoholism, irregulation of nutrition, infection of the intestinal tract, medical or industrial poisonous matters, intoxication, chronic cardiac insufficiency, etc. In traditional Chinese medicine, the disease is put into the category of tympanites, mass in the abdomen and internal mass.

1. Main Points for Diagnosis

a. The patient has a case history of virus hepatitis, snail fever, irregulation of nutrition or long-term drinking.

b. The patient shows the symptoms and bodily features

of hypofunction of the liver, such as a poor appetite, feeling exhausted, nausea, discomfort in the abdomen, vascular spiders and liver palms. With some cases, there may be the presence of jaundice.

c. The patient shows symptoms of portal hypertension, such as varices of the vein of the abdominal wall, splenomegalia, ascitic fluid, and hemorrhoid as well as varices of the fundus of the stomach and esophageal varicosis, both of which are observable through a barium swallow examination with a fluororscopy.

2. Clinical Types

a. The compensatory phase of the liver function: it is chiefly symptomized as hepato-splenomegaly and sclerotic texture usually with a complication of vascular spider and liver palm. However, with some cases, no obvious symptoms are shown at all, or the most striking features might be only feeling exhausted and a poor appetite. An examination might confirm that the liver function is within the normal range or only a little abnormal.

b. The decompensatory phase of the liver function: it is chiefly characterized by two types of clinic symptoms caused respectively by hypofunction of the liver and portal hypertension.

3. Methods of Diagnosis

Color and the Luster of the Palm

a. During the initial phase, the palm looks red, the contours of the blood vessels are distinctly visible, while during the advanced phase, the surface of the palm generally looks greenish yellow with dark red or purple spots on the large and small thenars, which will be decolored when pressed (see Fig. 218).

b. In the hand, there is the presence of pigmentation with spots looking black and being unevenly distributed, or, there may be the presence of vascular spiders.

c. In the area designated as *Xun*, the contour of the vein is visible and it extends directly toward the index finger (see Fig. 219).

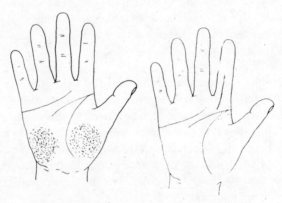

Fig. 218   **Fig. 219**

d. On Line 3 in the area designated as *Zhen*, the pulsing of the artery can be palpated (see Fig. 220).

e. On both sides of the thumb, prominences of the blood vessels can be observed (see Fig. 221).

f. The area designated as *Mingt'ang* (at the very center of the palm) bears a dark yellow color (see Fig. 222).

The Palmar Line

a. There is the presence of " ∗ "-shaped or " # "-shaped lines in the area designated as *Xun* (that on the right palm means more) (see Fig. 223).

b. Line 4 is deep and forms a "V" shape in coordination with the horizontal line at the conjunctive position of the areas designated as *Gen* and *Zhen* (see Fig. 224).

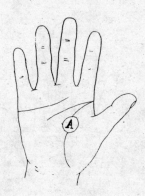

Fig. 220

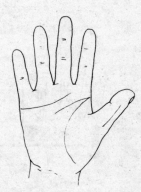

Fig. 221

Fig. 222

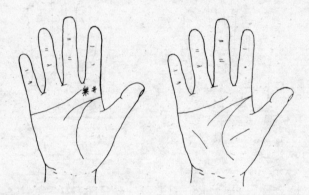

Fig. 223   Fig. 224

　c. The existence on Line 3 of the left palm of an insular line whose length is about 1/3 of that of Line 3 indicates hypersplenism in the phase of cirrhosis, while the symultaneous existence of such a line on both palms suggests a severe case in the decompensatory phase of cirrhosis (see Fig. 225).

　d. Most cases of cirrhosis wear a straight and long Line 9, which shows that the cases have to do with drinking (see Fig. 226).

　e. Line 6 which runs through the lower section of Line 3 is significant for the prognosis of a case. If Line 3 is intercepted by Line 6 and does not extend itself any more, it indicates a possible ending of life; if it is only cut through by Line 6, it suggests that at the age represented by the cutting, the case possibly will be worsened but will be able to be remitted (see Fig. 227).

The Nail

The nails look gray-pale and appear as anemic nails. On their surfaces there are stringed pearl-like prominences (see Fig. 228), while on the back of the nails there are yellow

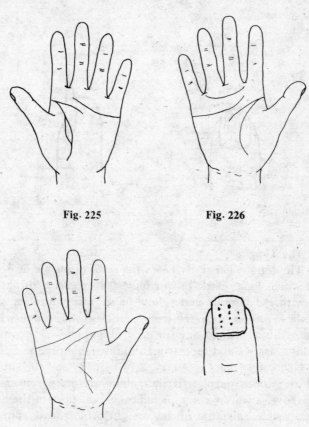

Fig. 225   Fig. 226

Fig. 227   Fig. 228

vertical folds (see Fig. 229). With some cases, the nails are ladle-shaped (see Fig. 230).

Fig. 229   Fig. 230

The Tongue

The tongue generally bears the color of purple or dark. One which looks dark brown indicates excessive drinking, one with red laterals and yellow or slightly white fur suggests a favorable recovery from cirrhosis, while one which looks red but without any fur on it often indicates a complication of ascites and forecasts an unfavorable prognosis.

Generally, there is sublingual varicosity and the sublingual area looks purple. If the sublingual mucosa near the vein shows a yellow color, it indicates the stasis of the bile. The possible existence of new or old hemorrhagic spots in that area often suggests a case of portal hypertension or the varicosity of the inferior vena cava and can serve as a warning of possible hemorrhage of the digestive tract.

Usually, there are large tracks of brown mucous patches

in the tunica intima of the upper lip together with prominently bulging small blood vessels

With cases of cirrhosis, the lips mostly become shrunk thin with a blue and rugose pheriphery. They are often cyanotic with the upper lip being more obvious than the lower one. Mostly, there are two downward-pointing wrinkles at the corners of the lips.

The Tooth

There is gingival bleeding and swelling, and the teeth become loose.

The Eye

Most cases of cirrhosis show ocular albinism in the upper or lower part of the eye with iris xanthochromia. A red blood vessel can be seen running across the whole right eye and the eyeball is viberating (see Fig. 231).

Fig. 231

The Ear

The ears are lusterless and the earlobes are shrunk. A

chondric proliferation as big as a grain of millet can be palpated at the point on the back of the right ear which is homologous with the liver acupoint of the ear.

The Facial Expression

The acupoint named Yint'ang looks blue-yellow, lusterless, and wrinkled. One who wears 1 or 3 vertical lines there is supposed to have a "flaming liver fire," and is subject to a violent temper, which is harmful to the disease, while one who wears 2 horizontal lines there are subject to worriness and "disorder of the liver-*qi*," and is apt to be in the sulks.

The complexion of such a case often looks dark or greenish yellow and the face often wears vascular spiders and "paper money" wrinkles. Most cases bear a complexion of consumative diseases. With a case of the biliary stasis type, the skin shows a greenish yellow color, which is particularly noticeable around the nose and the lips. On both sides of the nose bridge, there are brown skin patches which assume the form of a butterfly and, therefore, are alternately known as "butterfly patches." The nostrils are mostlt dry and subject to hemorrhage.

The Physical Form

With most cases of cirrhosis, the limbs are usually lean, the abdomen is bulging, and the skin is coarse. With the male sex, mastauxy, decrease in chaetae and shrink of the testis may be encountered, while with the female sex, menstrual disorder and cutaneous pigmentation may be encountered. With both sexes, varicose vein can be observed in the abdominal wall and the periphery of the umbilicus.

Appendicitis

Appendicitis, which is divided into two types, i. e. , the

acute and the chronic, is encountered in any age group of people, but 40% of all the cases take place among people between 20 and 40 of age with male cases being two times more than female cases. In traditional Chinese medicine, this disease is known as "periappendicular abscess."

1. Main points for Diagnosis

a. A wandering pain in the right side of the lower abdomen: among all such cases, 70% to 80% show such a typical abdominal pain. In the initial phase, the inflammation is limited in the submucous layer of the appendix and is symptomatic of a pain in the periphery of the umbilicus or in the upper abdomen, as it is caused by the reflexion of the splanchnic nerves. Therefore, the patient finds it difficult to accurately point out the location of the pain. Only when the inflammation has developed to the serous coat of the appendix and begins to irritate the parietal perotoneum which is controlled by the body nerves, can the patient locate the pain precisely in the lower abdomen. This can serve as an important basis for the diagnosis of acute appendicitis.

b. Tenderness: Most keen is the tenderness in the right lower abdomen, and usually, the point of the tenderness is located at the position of 1/3 away from the intersection of the navel and the tie line of the anterior superior iliac spine on the right side, known as the "McBurney's point." However, this may vary due to the different locations of the appendix.

c. Rebound tenderness and tension of the abdominal muscle: In examining, when the hand which presses the patient's abdomen is abruptly taken away, the patient immediately feels a sharp pain. Such a pain is known as "rebound tenderness." That is because the pain results from the viberation of the peritoneum caused by the irritation of the inflammation. The tension of the abdominal muscle also signifies that the inflammation has already expanded out of the appendix and begun to irritate the peritoneum, which induces the reflexion and protective shrink of the muscle of the abdominal wall. When the inflammation has become more severe or perforating, there is usually apparent tension of the abdominal muscle.

2. Methods of Diagnosis

The Physical Form

Particular physical features which often appear in a case of appendicitis are chiefly observed in the neck, the shoulders and the feet:

One whose neck tends to tilt toward the right side and slightly protruding forward shows that he or she suffers from chronic inflammation in the laryngeal part of the pharynx. There are those who habitually swallow down their own sputum so that the bacteria invades the appendix and proliferates in and gives rise to the inflammation of the appendix. So, most cases of chronic appendicitis are complicated with chronic laryngopharyngitis.

Those who have round and sloping shoulders constitute quite a number of cases of appendicitis.

Those who exert energy onto the tip of the right foot in walking are apt to contract appendicitis. Such persons, once they have contracted appendicitis, often have a shrunk right leg, which may give unbearable pain to the patient when forcefully stretched.

The Finger

The numbness of the fingers indicates a severe case of appendicitis. In such a case, even pricked with a needle, the patient will not feel a pain in the finger.

The Palmar Line

In the area between Line 2 and the area designated as *Dui*, there are disordered lines, which mostly assume checkered rectangular frames. After an appendectomy, this frame will become more noticeable (see Fig. 232)

The Lip

With a case of chronic appendicitis complicated with peritoneal glutination, the cementation between the lip and the gum is observable when the upper lip is turned up.

The Ear

In the cochlear part of the ear there are blue contours of blood vessels bulging out and their possible branches may be observed (see Fig. 233).

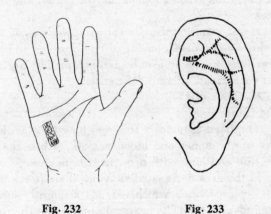

Fig. 232   Fig. 233

Inanition Syndrome in Infant

Inanition is a syndrome resulting from deficiency of various nutritional elements, can be inconsecutively encountered in different diseases, and shows various symptoms. This disease of infantile inanition occurs mostly among infants and children below the age of three. It is caused by the fact that infants and children are developing rapidly and need more nutritional matters while they are relatively imperfect in their digestive function and thus are apt to be affected by external conditions.

1. Chief Symptoms

Inanition in the initial phase is chiefly symptomized as a stagnant state of the weight of the body, which gradually develops into the loss of the fat within the body and hence a loss of weight. Generally, the loss of the subcutaneous fat takes place in the following sequence: first in the buttock, then in the trunk, the abdomen and the limbs, and finally in the cheeks.

A case of inanition usually shows such signs as paleness in the skin, underdevelopment of the muscles and a feeble muscular tension. It can also be accompanied by anemia, nutritional edema and vitamin deficiencies.

2. Methods of Diagnosis

The Hand

a. The hand assumes a thin and long form with visible contours of the bones and blood vessels, while the fingers are also thin and long with prominent knuckles.

b. In the area designated as *Xun*, there is the presence of a blue-colored line, which extends straightly upward along the index finger. The nearer it approaches the tip of the finger, the severer the case it indicates is.

c. The area designated as *Gen* looks greenish pale with loose muscles.

d. There are distinctly visible contours of blood vessels in the portion of the wrist.

e. With a case who has been suffering from malnutrition since its fetal phase, there is the presence of branching on Line 2 or the discontinuation of the extending line of Line 2.

f. Line 3 is shallow, short and on and off.

(For all the above-mentioned features, please see Fig. 234)

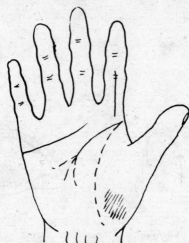

Fig. 234

The Nail

The nails are thin and fragile without the semilunar flaps. There are dotted small pits on the surface of the nails, and there are inverted thorns near the roots of the nails, such infants and children like to bite on their nails (see Fig. 235).

The Eye

There is the presence of blue-colored small spots at the endings of the small blood vessels in the iris (see Fig. 236).

The Tongue

Such a case usually has a geographic tongue and often has contracted stomatitis.

The Ear

In the representing areas on the ear respectively for the

Fig. 235   **Fig. 236**

stomach, intestine and abdomen, there are visible contours of blood vessels, while in the area on the back of the ear homologous to the stomach portion there are granules as big as grains of millet.

The Facial Expression

The forehead is wrinkled, the zygomatic bones are protruding, and the neck is thin and long, thus giving the impression of a big head. The hairs are yellow-brown and few or assume the form of ears of wheat. The skin is dry and desquamative, and the infant looks like an old person, known as "senial look."

The Abdomen

The abdominal vein becomes prominent, and the vicinity of the navel bears a yellow color. The navel itself presents a long form, and its secretion increases. The abdomen becomes huge and bulging.

Bacillary Dysentery

Bacillary dysentery is a commonly encountered infectious disease of the intestinal tract caused by Bacillus dysenteriae. Its major pathologic change is symptomatic of defuse inflammation of the colon. It may be contracted any time throughout the year, but is generally epidemic in summer and fall. The population has a universal susceptibility to such a disease, and there is a higher disease incidence among children and youths. Clinically, it is divided into two types, i. e. , the acute and the chronic. In traditional Chinese medicine, it is generally categorized as dysentery. Acute bacillary dysentary generally belongs to the type of warm and heat pathogens, while chronic bacillary dysentery is pretty alike with protracted dysentery or recurrent dysentery. Due to the fact that acute bacillary dysentery attacks abruptly and develops rapidly and can be cured thoroughly, the palmar lines and the hand features do not show any noticeable changes. Here in this section, emphasis is to be laid upon the recommendation of the methods for the diagnosis of chronic bacillary dysentery through observing the features of the hand.

1. Clinical Types

A case of dysentery which lasts or has lasted for a duration of more than two months is regarded as chronic dysentery, which, clinically, can be divided into the following 3 types:

a. The chronic persisting type:

(1) The patient has a case history of acute bacillary dysentery which has not been cured but exists persistently;

(2) The patient shows, by different degrees, such symptoms as abdominal pain, abdominal distention and diarrhea

211

or an alternate presence of diarrhea and constipation, often with mucus stool or pus and blood stool;

(3) Through stool cultivation, the Bacillus dysenteriae registers a positive reaction.

b. The acute attack type:

In the course of a case of chronic dysentery, an acute attack may often be induced by catching cold, taking in cold food and drink or fatigue. Its major symptoms include abdominal pain, diarrhea, pus and blood stool and fever in the face, being free of any distinct general toxemic symptoms.

c. The chronic latent type:

(1) The patient has a case history of dysentery but has not shown any clinical symptoms for a considerable period of time;

(2) Through a microscopy of the sigmoid colon, it may be observed that the intestinal mucosa is granule-shaped and that an ulcer or polpy has been formed. Through a stool culture, the Bacillus dysenteriae registers a positive reaction.

2. Methods of Diagnosis

The Hand

a. The fingers are thin and long, and there are relatively broad gaps between them when the fingers are put together. The index finger has become apparently thin.

b. The muscles in the area designated as *Zhen* are loose and sagging with "×"-shaped lines (see Fig. 237).

c. The area designated as *Gen* bears a greenish pale color with a distinct blue contour of the blood vessel and flat and hollow muscles. Besides, there is a deep and long line which remarkably divides the areas designated as *Zhen* and *Gen* (see Fig. 238).

d. With the thumb as the center, the hand as a whole bends toward the little finger.

e. There is the presence of abnormal lines in the part of

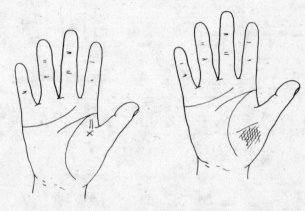

Fig. 237   **Fig. 238**

the area designated as *Dui* close to the acupoint Mingt'ang (see Fig. 239).

    f. There is the presence of relatively deep Line 4 (see Fig. 240).

    g. The existence of Line 6 in arc forms and their running across the space between Line 2 and Line 3 indicate digestive disorder caused by irregulated diet. And so, such symptoms as eructation with fetid odor, indigestion, diarrhea, borborygmus, etc. can all be encountered (see Fig. 241).

    h. The root segment of the ring finger looks pale and dry, the acupoint Mingt'ang and the representing area for the lower abdomen look pale in color, and their color of blood recovers very slow after they are pressed, all these suggest a prolonged case of diarrhea or loose stool.

    i. The dark blue color found in both the large and the

213

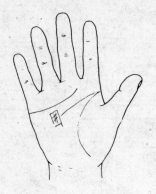

Fig. 239

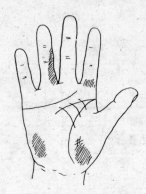

Fig. 240

Fig. 241

small thenar reveals the pathogenic cause of catching a cold which has invaded the spleen and stomach. A high temperature at the center of the palm which is obviously moist reveals the pathogenic cause of retention of food in the stomach and intestine, while a low temperature at the center of the palm and the root segment of the little finger and the area designated as *Kan* being pale and lusterless reveal generally a case of diarrhea caused by insufficiency of the kidney-*yang* (see Fig. 241).

The Nail

The nails of such a case are usually free of any semilunar flaps and look light in color with their root parts looking pale or blue-purple. Or, the nails are spoon-shaped. With a prolonged case, there may be horizontal ditches and ridges on the nail surface with pterygium or pathologic mass.

The Eye

The pupils of such cases are usually small and are apt to take an outward slant vision. Besides, the existence of light blue spots may be observed on the endings of the blood vessels of the conjunctiva.

The Lip

Patients of bacillary dysentery tend to have a dry mouth and lips or canker sores. The two laterals in the central part of the upper lip is known as tunica intima of the upper lip. With a case of chronic bacillary dysentery, the tunica intima looks dark blue in color, and its coloring is supposed to tell of the difference in the severity and the length of the duration of the case.

The Ear

With a case of chronic bacillary dysentery, the prominence of the blood vessels can be observed at the area for the abdominal cavity on the ear, and the prominent nodule can be palpated at the acupoints for the colon and for the stomach

on the ear. Or, its desquamation
may also be observed. Usually,
the ear looks pale and dry (see
Fig. 242).

The Tongue

Generally, the tongue bears
a dark purple color. One with the
impairment of body fluids is free
of any tongue fur; one with the
damp-heat wears yellow fur; one
with cold-damp wears white fur;
one with insufficiency of saltness
in the body wears thick fur; one

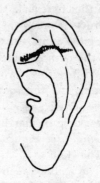

Fig. 242

with excessive saltness in the body is free of any fur; and
one accompanied with a low fever has scarlet laterals of the
tongue. With anyone who wears yellow, thick and sticky
tongue fur, it indicates unexceptionally the existence of stagnant stool in the intestine. Although the patient may be suffering from diarrhea, a treatment by purgation is still appli-
cable.

One whose sublingual vein bears a blue-purple color
and becomes thicker or lumbricoid has contracted distinct inflammation in the intestinal tract caused by the obstruction
in the hepato-enteric circulation resulting from the protracted diarrhea. If, symultaneously, there is the existence of um-
brella-shaped distribution of very small and thin blood vessels under the tongue, it signifies the occurrence of the atrophy of the intestinal mucosa caused by chronic diarrhea.

The Facial Expression

A case of acute bacillary dysentery is apt to develop into
a case of bacillary dysentery of the chronic type, if he or she
wears the following facial features: a pale complexion, a long
and narrow face, a lean stature with deeply hollowed eyes.

216

Clinically, such a face belongs to the ulcer type. Such persons usually speak in a thin and low voice and has a forward protruding chin; the lower jaw assumes the shape of an obtuse angle; and the legs are thin, long and hairless.

With a case of chronic bacillary dysentery who has suffered from prolonged diarrhea, if the acupoint Jenchung and its vicinity bear a color of blue or slight darkness, then, it indicates that the disease was caused by the impairment of overeating.

Constipation

Constipation is a pathologic condition of the bowels in which the feces are dry and hardened and evacuation is difficult and infrequent. Clinically, it may either occur individually or be concomitant with other diseases. In traditional Chinese medicine, it is known as *yang* constipation, *yin* constipation or spleno constipation, all of which are generally divided into the heat type, the *qi* type, the insufficiency type and the cold type.

1. Clinical Types

a. The stagnation of feces in the left abdomen is called left constipation. The retainment of the feces in the sigmoid colon, which usually shows indistinct symptoms, tends to give rise to diseases which occur below the diaphragm and in the lower part of the body. Such a case always has an irregular bowel movement, e. g. , once in every 3, 5 or even 10 days.

b. The stagnation of the feces in the right abdomen is called right constipation. The retainment of the feces at the appendix tends to give rise to diseases which occur above the diaphragm and in the upper part of the body and appendicitis. Such cases are often encountered among children, who, symptomatically, have the desire to defecate everyday but have frequently failed in evacuation of bowels.

2. Chief Symptoms

a. a constant feeling of exhaustedness and dizziness

b. frequent yawning and a failing memory

c. a gradual turn into the purple color in the face

d. a pain in the back and waist, especially a pain in the lumboscral portion.

3. Methods of Diagnosis

The Physical Form

a. A case of left constipation who carries stagnant feces in the sigmoid colon is apt to develop a "water snake" waist, and favors to look downward. In walking, the left foot tends to incline outward and the steps are heavy.

b. With a case of right constipation, the cheekbones are prominent, and the eyeballs are lifted up, forming the so-called "albinotic eyes. " The upper body bends forward into a posture in which as though one were reading somebody a lecture.

The Palm and the Fingers

A palm manifesting distinctly bulging veins indicates the existence of stagnant feces in the intestine (see Fig. 243).

a. The right palm with visible blue contours of blood vessels signifies the existence of the stagnation at the appendix.

b. The fingers of the right hand with visible blue contours of blood vessels signifies the existence of the satgnation in the colon.

c. The left palm with visible blue contours of blood vessels signifies the existence of the stagnation in the sigmoid colon.

d. The fingers of the left hand bearing observable blue

contours of blood vessels signifies the existence of the stagnation in the descending colon.

The Palmar Line

a. The area designated as *Gen* bears a color of greenish blue, and there is the presence of varicose veins on the palm. One who wears such features on the left palm tends to defecate once every 2, 3 or more days, while with a case who wears such features on the right palm, his or her feces are dry and hardened, and the evacuation is difficult, although he or she defecates everyday.

b. There is the presence of quite a number of branching lines on Line 3 (see Fig. 244). If there are the presence of

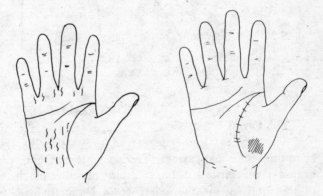

Fig. 243	**Fig. 244**

branching lines on Line 3 and symultaneous changes in the color of the hand, then, it indicates that the constipation has already affected one's health and has caused some other diseases.

c. In the vicinity of Line 3, there is the formation of a

thin and small secondary line (see Fig. 245).

The Nail

The nails look darkly yellow or pale and lusterless, and there is the presence of deep and uneven vertical stripes on the nail of the thumb. With some cases, this nail looks darkly brown (see Fig. 246).

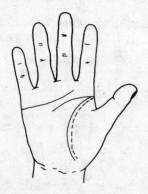 

Fig. 245   Fig. 246

The Facial Expression

The dryness and paleness of the upper lip are both symptoms of constipation. The possible existence of white granular vegetations as big as grains of millet on the tie link of the lip suggests the existence of hemorrhoid caused by constipation.

A case of constipation often purses the lips closely into a "—" shape.

A prolonged case of constipation is susceptible to the obstruction of the brain function, such as dizziness, headache and declining memory. There may be the presence of darkly yellow spots on the forehead, which is generally lusterless. However, after the remission of the constipation, the luster on the forehead will be recovered.

With infants and children who suffer from constipation, there may be the presence of blue bulging contours of blood vessels between the eyebrows. That is also the symptom of the stagnation of meconium during the neonatal period. Such infants and children are susceptible to ,besides constipation, common cold and indigestion.

Itching of the nasal mucosa on the right side suggests the dryness of the small intestine, while itching of the nasal mucosa on the left side suggests the dryness of the large intestine. Both kinds of itching are caused by the irritation of the trigeminal nerve by the hardened feces through the channel of the nerve conduction. With infants and children, nasal hemorrhage may be caused by digging the nose with a finger. Based upon the bleeding nostril, the portion where the stagnation of the feces can be judged.

The Tongue Fur

Stagnation of feces is symptomatic of a thick, yellow or dark brown tongue fur. In such a case, the stagnant feces should be excreted as soon as possible ,and once the stagnant feces in the intestine are evacuated, will the tongue fur disappear.

Hemorrhoids

Hemorrhoids is a venous dilatation inside the anal sphincter of the rectum and beneath the mucous membrane, or outside the anal sphincter and beneath the surface of the skin. It is mostly encountered among adults and cases of constipation. In accordance with the different locations of the existence of homorrhoids, it can be divided into external hemorrhoids, internal hemorrhoids and mixed hemorrhoids. That which can be observed from without is called external hemorrhoids, that which is located within the anus and cannot be observed with ordinary means is called internal hemorrhoids. Both kinds of hemorrhoids, except for their different locations, share the same pathogenic factors and therapies.

There are quite a number of pathogenic factors causing hemorrhoids, such as irregulated diet, excessive eating of pungent food, smoking, drinking, long-time standing or sitting in work, habitual constipation, low spirits, pregnancy, etc.

1. Chief Symptoms

Simple external hemorrhoids generally does not show any distinct symptoms, except for a foreign body sensation or a feeling of fullness after long-time standing or walking. When there is thrombosis with a case of external hemorrhoids, there may be in the anus portion a pain, which will be worsened when the patient is walking or defecating. Simple internal hemorrhoids generally does not give any discomfort at all, and a pain is not its chief symptom. Its chief symptom is hemorrhage:.during the initial phase, the bleeding is only little, but with the enlargement of the swelling of the hemorrhoids, there will be more bleeding. Hardened feces, fatigue, drinking and excessive taking in pungent food are usually the inducing factors for hemorrhage.

2. Methods of Diagnosis

The Palmar Line

a. Along the inner side of Line 3, there are downward-pointing, plume-shaped branches (see Fig. 247), while on Line 3 of the left palm there is the presence of long and narrow insular lines (see Fig. 248).

222

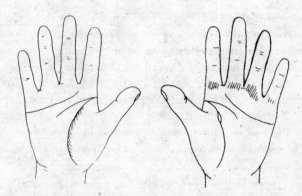

b. The root portions of the fingers bear a light black color. The light black color which appears at the root portions of the fingers of the left hand indicates that the hemorrhoid is located at the left side of the anus, while that which appears at the portions on the right hand indicates that the hemorrhoid is located at the right side of the anus (see Fig. 248).

The Lip

With cases of hemorrhoids, the lips are favorably pursed closely and form a "—" shape. And an opening mouth is rarely seen. Those whose mouths are tightly closed have tightly closed anuses accordingly. The lips usually bear a color of purple, or with purple spots or they are crooked. With the upper lip being lifted up, white or yellow vegetations may be observed on the tie link of the upper lip.

Chronic Glomerular Nephritis

Chronic glomerular nephritis is called for short chronic nephritis, and its pathogeny remains unidentified. Cases of chronic nephritis developed into or resulting from acute nephritis constitute only a small number, while most of such cases are caused by unidentified pathogenic factors. However, generally, it is believed that it is caused by immunoreaction. Chronic nephritis is mostly encountered among adults. In the light of its clinical symptoms, it belongs to the category of edema and consumative disease in traditional Chinese medicine.

1. Main Points for Diagnosis

a. With most of the cases, a latency is shown of the onset of the disease, while only a few cases have a history of acute nephritis.

b. Clinically, this disease is symptomatic of various degrees of proteinuria, microscopic hematuria, hypertension, edema and impairment of the renal function, and during its advanced phase, there may be the presence of anemia, retinal degeneration and uremia.

c. During the course of chronic nephritis, an acute attack may be induced by such a factor as infection of the respiratory tract and may show similar symptoms to those of acute nephritis. But there are some cases which are remitted automatically.

2. Clinical Types

a. The ordinary type: it is the type most commonly encountered among all the cases of chronic nephritis.

(1) a slight or moderate edema, which may be accompanied with a moderate elevation of the blood pressure.

(2) the presence of moderate degree proteinuria ($+-+$ $+$) through a urine test. Through a uropsammus counting, the RBC often registers more than 10. A high power field and various degree cyclindruia.

(3) a certain degree impairment of the renal function, a lowering of the creatinine clearance rate, a lowering of the phenolsulfonphthalein excretion rate, an increase in nocturia, a weakening of the urine concentrating power, with the specific gravity of urine being lower than 1. 015, and a-zotemia.

(4) Most of such cases have a feeling of exhaustedness, a soreness in the waist, being often accompanied with anemia.

b. The nephropathic type:

(1) Such cases show all the symptoms of a nephritic syndrome: a great quantity of proteinuria (73. 5/24 hrs.); few plasma proteins, with the albumin often being less than 3% g. ; noticeable edema; and/or an increase in the gravity of the plasma cholesterol.

(2) There is the presence of microscopic hematuria or hypertension and progressive impairment of the renal function.

c. The hypertensive type:

(1) There is the existence of all the symptoms manifested by the ordinary type, but it is characterized by a persistent moderate degree elevation of the blood pressure (especially the elevation of the diastolic pressure).

(2) There is a relatively slight edema and urinary change, a moderate-degree or more severe impairment of the renal function.

(3) A fundus examination may reveal that the retinal artery is narrow and tortuous, that the light reflexion is intensified, and that there is the phenomenon of arteriovenous

crossing and oppressing and the existence of flocculent exudate.

3. Methods of Diagnosis

The color and Luster of the Palm

Usually, the palm of such a case is fat, fair and clear, the small thenar is particularly plump and prominent, and all the mounts are higher than the surface of the palm. The skin on the palm is lustrous and delicate, with that in the area designated as *Gen* bearing a color of dark blue (see Fig. 249). Both the areas designated as *Xun* and *Kun* are usually noticeably prominent (see Fig. 250), and they look either red and moist or pale. In all these areas, the contours of the veins are observable. With an initial case, these areas look scarlet, while with a prolonged one, they look pale.

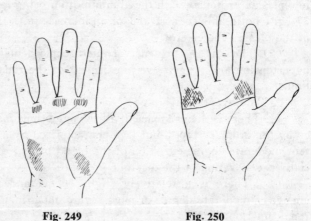

Fig. 249   **Fig. 250**

The Palmar Line

a. Due to the dropsy of the hand of such a case, changes in the form of small and thin lines are few and indistinct.

However, in the area designated as *Kun*, relatively deep and neatly arranged vertical lines may be observed (see Fig. 251).

    b. With a prolonged case, at the ending of Line 3 there is the presence of small insular lines, or the line itself becomes curved, absent or shallower.

    c. The area encircled by Line 3 is relatively large, while that by Line 1 is relatively small. With the middle finger as the center, the hand as a whold bends toward the thumb.

    d. The presence of two vertical lines which run through Line 1 beneath the ring finger indicates a case of chronic nephritis of the hypertensive type (see Fig. 252).

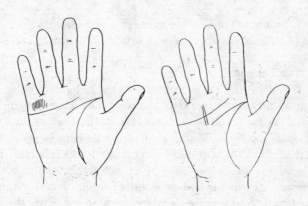

Fig. 251   Fig. 252

The Nail

The nails of such a case generally look pale, and are mostly free of any semilunar flaps. Hollow nails (see Fig. 253), spoon-shaped nails (see Fig. 254) and horizontal-ditched nails (see Fig. 255) are often found. Generally, the

nails of such cases are coarse in texture, lusterless and fragile.

The Tongue

Usually, the tongue of such cases is light in color and plump in form with marks of the teeth. At its root there is a little thick fur, and with most cases, the tongue fur looks gray-pale and thin. With a case of impairment in several internal organs, the texture of the tongue looks relatively red, while with a prolonged case of uremia, the tongue will be cyanotic, free of fur and deficient of fluid. If the tongue is coated with blue-purple or black fur, it indicates that the case is difficult to recover.

Generally, there is a varicose sublingual vein, which looks light in color.

The Lip

The light color of the tunica intima of the upper lip suggests a case of chronic nephritis with anemia, while its red color suggests the injury of the *yin* by the kidney disease so that the gum is often swollen with gingival hemorrhage.

The Ear

The earlobes look thin in form and brown in color.

The Eye

In the eyelids, there is the presence of dropsy, which is worse in the morning than in the afternoon. The eyes look obliquely inward, while the lacrimal passages are swollen with bulging veins. Owing to the fact that the fluid within the body of such a patient can moisten the throat successively, the patient has a resonant voice and desirable eloquence.

The Facial Expression

As the upper area of the forehead has to do with the kidney, that area of a case of chronic nephritis bears a color of gray with blurred clotches observable under the lower edge of the hairs. If that area of the forehead looks dark, the chin is usually dark accordingly.

With a case of kidney diseases, there is dropsy in the face as soon as getting up in the morning, but it will begin to extinct in the afternoon. Along with the advancement of the case, however, the dropsy will become worsened further. A severe case of dropsy often has a pair of up-lifted eyes, a dull look or a nailed gaze in a certain direction. Furthermore, some such cases may wear a wry mouth, and the " ⁄＼ " - shaped wrinkles between the eye-brows may get closely together. According to the degrees by which the dropsy presents itself, the severity of the cases can be differentiated. With a severe case, the puffy lower lids look dark purple, the forehead appears sordid, and dim blotches may be observed there (see Fig. 256).

The lower part of the face is usually ectatic, and the body is plump and fat. One who has a broad space between the pupils has often developed some kidney disease caused by supernutrition and often accompanied with hypertension.

Most cases of kidney diseases, however, are featured with long and narrow faces, broad spaces between the pupils and the eyeballs.

A case of nephritis often wears purely white and delicately fine skin, which itches after sweating, and few hairs on the head.

The Physical Form

With a case of rental dysfunction, the body tends to bend forward in walking, and the waist tends to turn in a backward lower direction.

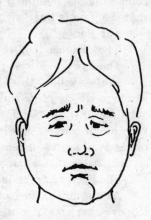

Fig. 256

Besides, there is tenderness in the 10th thoracic vertebrae.

The Foot

One whose sole of the shoe for the left foot is worn all the more along the rear outer edge can be identified with the location of the focus in the right kidney, while reversely, that of the shoe for the right foot is worn all the more along the rear outer edge can be identified with the location of the focus in the left kidney. At the same time, one who has trouble in the left kidney has a left thicker ankle, while one who has trouble in the right kidney has a thicker right ankle. Moreover, a patient of kidney diseases has an excessively broad space between the tibia and the fibula, so that when he or she turns the ankle first inward and then outward, the movement is inflexible. The side on which the inflexibility occurs in turning the ankle indicates the side on which the disease exists in the kidney there.

Urinary Tract Infection and Pyelonephritis

Urinary tract infection usually refers to the flammatory pathologic change by the direct invasion of bacteria into the urinary system. Generally, it is divided into the lower urinary tract infection and the upper urinary tract infection, such as cystitis and pyelonephritis.

Pyelonephritis is the suppurative inflammation caused by the invasion of the bacteria into the renal pelvis, the renal tubules and the interrenal tissues. It is a common kind of disease among urinary tract infection. Clinically, the disease covers two phases, i. e., the acute phase and the chronic phase. It is often encountered among the female sex, mostly among women of child-bearing age. Clinically, in the terminology of traditional Chinese medicine, this disease belongs to the category of stranguria and lumbago due to the kidney deficiency.

1. Clinical Types

a. Acute Pyelonephritis

(1) Usually an abrupt onset of the disease and with such general symptoms as feeling chilly, high fever (the temperature may be as high as over 38℃), general malaise, headache, asthenopia, nausea, and vomiting. A light case, however, may show indistinct symptoms.

(2) Frequency of micturination, urgency of urination, urodynia, and a waist pain which may turn down to the pudendum from the abdomen.

(3) A purcussion pain in the kidney area, a tenderness at the costolumbar point (at the intersection of the greater psoas muscle with the 12th rib), and tenderness at the upper uriniferous point (at the bandage of the lower navel outside

the straight muscle of the abdomen) and in the area of the bladder.

(4) An increase in the number of white cells and the neutrophil in the blood, the existence of large quantity of white cells in the urinary sediments, occasionally observable leukocytic cast, and the discovery of bacteria in about a percentage of 90 of the urinary sediments through a smear chromoscopy.

b. Chronic Pyelonephritis

(1) A reccurrrence or protraction of a case of acute pyelonephritis for a duration of more than one year.

(2) With some cases, no distinct symptoms can be found during the acute phase except for such slight symptoms as a low fever, asthenopia, a poor appetite, anemia, soreness and pain in the waist, low frequency of urination, and such positive physical features as purcussion pain in the kidney portion and tenderness at the costo-lumbar point.

(3) Through repeated routine urine tests, a few white cells or pus cells are found, a urinary bacterial culture shows positive reaction, and the counting of bacteria in the urine $\geqslant$ 10. 5 per ml.

(4) There is a persisting impairment of the renal tubules, which is symptomatic of diuresis, nocturia, hyposthenuria and renal tubular acidosis.

(5) Through an intravenous pyelography, if the pyelic calix is found deformed or narrowed, the surface of the kindney is found uneven or both kidneys are found unequal in size, the diagnosis can be confirmed.

2. Methods of Diagnosis

The Color and Luster of the Palm

There are on the plam patchy aulas which mostly appear at the lower section of the area designated as *Qian* and in the lower section designated as *Gen*. The area designated as *Kan* looks bluish pale, while blue contours of blood vessels are visible on the wrist. The little finger looks thin and feeble, and compared with the other four fingers, it is redder or distinctly bright pale. The area designated as *Kun* is prominent or sagging, and both features show the susceptibility to diseases of the bladder urinary system. When the onset of acute pyelonephritis is accompanied with general symptoms, there is an elevation of the temperature at the center of the palm, which usually wears reticular blue contours of blood vessles, most distincly in the area representing the kidney and in the little finger (see Fig. 257).

Fig. 257

The Palmar Line

a. In ,the section of Line 1 ranging from the ring finger to the little finger, there is the presence of thin and disordered lines or chain-like lines (see Fig. 258).

b. In the area designated as *Kun*, there are neatly arranged "川" -shaped lines or " # " -shaped and " ∗ " -shaped lines (see again Fig. 258).

c. A particularly long Line 11 is observable and straightly entends itself toward under the ring finger often with " # " -shaped lines on it (see Fig. 259).

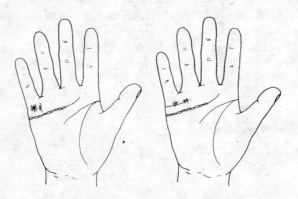

Fig. 258   Fig. 259

d. The possible symultaneous presence of Line 9 indicates that the case has a feeble function of the bladder urinary system (see Fig. 260).

e. Sometimes there is the presence of Line 6 which cuts horizontally through Line 3 (see Fig. 260 and Fig. 261).

The Nail

The nails are gray-pale, dry and lusterless with turbid semilunar flaps, or they may also have spots, black vertical stripes or ridges (see Fig. 262).

The Tongue

The tongue is mostly coated with a thin fur.

The Ear

There are red or blue contours of bulging blood vessles

in the cochlear of the ear (see Fig. 263).

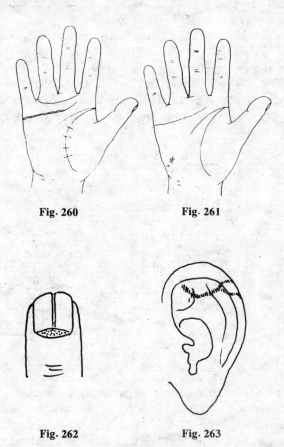

Fig. 260 Fig. 261

Fig. 262 Fig. 263

The Facial Expression

The acupoint Yint'ang seems to be covered with a layer of dark gray color and looks turbid.

Most of such cases wear long and narrow faces with broad spaces between the two puplis and especially those between the two eyeballs (see Fig. 264).

The red color borne in the area from under the tip of the nose to the edge of the upper lip signifies the stage of fervescence of a case of acute pyelonephritis (see Fig. 265).

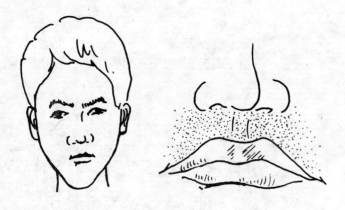

Fig. 264	Fig. 265

The blue color in the acute stage signifies that the case is accompanied with pain in the renal portion and frequent urination, while the yellow color signifies a case of chronic pyelonephritis, and the bright white color indicates recurrence of the disease.

The Physical Form

Nephritis can be observed by examining the soles of one's shoes: if the heel part of the sole of the shoe is apparently worn, it indicates the existence of some disease in the ureter or in the bladder wall. If that part of the sole is worn at the rear inner side of the right foot, it indicates the existence of the disease in the right side ureter and the right side bladder wall. If that worn part of the sole is located at the rear outer side of the left shoe, it indicates the existence of the disease in the left kidney. If the worn part of the sole is located at the rear outer side of the right foot, it indicates the existence of the disease in the right kidney.

Enuresis

Voluntary urination, as a complicated physiological mechanism of the human body, is a reflective action controlled by the urinary central nerve of the cerebrum. The reflex center is located at the sacral vertebra. When the volume of urine in the bladder reaches a certain amount, the pressure in the bladder elevates rapidly, and the corresponding reflection in the brain is given rise to, known as "precipitant urination," so that a vigorous impulsive sense is transmitted to the spinal cord. Then, the reflex center sends out a motional impulse which causes the shrink of the anuretic muscle and the relaxation of the external sphincter and the perineal muscles. Thus, the urine is excreted from the bladder, and such a mechanism is known as reflective urination. Children under 2 or 3 years of age have only the mechanism of reflective urination and cannot urinate voluntarily, while children above 2 or 3 years of age and adults whose urinary reflex center has already begun to function can, by different degrees, control the so-called precipitant urination, repress the the reflective urination and urinate whenever they want to (i. e. , voluntary urination). However, a child who is more than 3 years of age and still cannot constantly control its urination is regarded as a case of enuresis, which, if happening at night, is alternately known as nocturia.

Methods of Diagnosis

The Palmar Line

a. The area designated as *Kan* is sagging, the palm looks pale, while the little finger is thin and soft.

b. Line 2 is relatively long.

c. There is the presence of quite a number of thin and disordered lines at the center of the palm.

d. There are quite some thin vertical stripes above Line 3 beneath the little finger.

(For all the above-mentioned features, please see Fig. 266).

The Eye

The eyeballs are covered with some thin and small red thread.

The Ear

There are quite a few bulging contours of very small blood vessels in the auricles, and the ears are thin and soft.

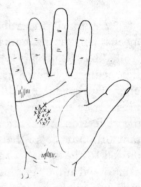

Fig. 266

The Facial Expression

Children suffering from enuresis look yellowish pale in the face with a distinct yellow color at the acupoint Yint'ang and around the nose, and their eyes are usually look dull.

Hyperthyroidism

Hyperthyroidism is a common disease of the internal secretion caused by hypersecretion of thyroxin. It is often encountered among the female sex, and the proportion of the incidences between the male sex and the female sex is about 1 : 4 to 1 : 6. This disease may occur among any age groups, but mostly among those between the age of 20 and 40. Clinically, the most commonly encountered types are the diffuse virutent goiter (also known as exophthalmic goiter) and the nodular virutent goiter. In the terminology of traditional Chinese medicine, it belongs to the category of goiter-*qi*.

1. Main Points for Diagnosis

a. The hypermetabolistic syndrome shows such symptoms as overeating, constant hunger, fear for hotness, hyperhidrosis, asthenosia and loss of weight.

b. The sympathetic excitative syndrome shows such symptoms as unstable morale, irascible temperament, failure in concentrating the mind, insomnia, tachycardia, increase in the pulse pressure, slight viberation of the hand when opened and hyperreflexia.

c. The difference bewteen the diffuse virutent goiter and the nodular virutent goiter lies in that the former is more often encountered among young women, who show diffuse thyroid enlargement, increase in the intaking 131 I, but the scanned is only the intaking 131 I in the nodular region, while that of the normal thyroid tissues around the region is repressed. Exophthalmus and dermopathic changes are rarely encountered, while the rate of occurrence of complications of the heart diseases is high, such as artrial fibrillation.

2. Methods of Diagnosis

The Eye

The eyeballs are bulging noticeably, and sometimes exophthalmus occurs on one side or in a single eye, while the eye will bulge afterwards. The fissures in the eyelids are widened and glossy, and both eyes can hardly close perfectly. Due to the fact that the upper lids are shrunk back, they tend to be unable to follow the eyeballs to turn and hang downward when the eyes look downward; when the eyes look upward, the forehead skin tends to fail in wrinkling up, thus forming the so-called "albinic eyes" in the lower parts. Nictitation is decreased, while convergence is insufficient (see Fig. 267).

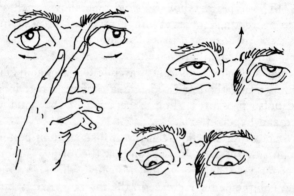

Fig. 267

The Color and Luster of the Palm

The hand viberates when stretched out, the palm looks red, and there is the presence of high temperature at the center of the palm. The skin is moist with sweat, and the red color of the palm is not evenly and equally distributed across the palm, as the root portion of the middle finger and the large and small thenars are noticeably redder. There is the presence of scarlet spots on both the large and the small thenar, and the area designated as *Xun* is prominent (see Fig. 268).

240

The Palmar Line

a. There is the presence of relatively deep Line 4 (see Fig. 269).

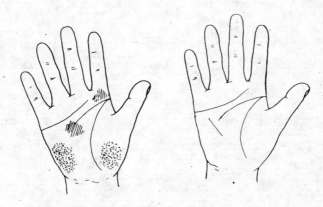

Fig. 268   **Fig. 269**

b. There are insular lines on Line 9 (see Fig. 270).

c. There is the presence of very large insular lines in the area of Line 2 close to Line 3 (see Fig. 271).

d. There are thin and scattered " + " -shaped and " * " -shaped lines (see Fig. 272).

e. The area designated as *Li* is prominent, while that designated as *Kan* is sagging. The former looks red, while the latter looks pale. Besides, there are " * " -shaped lines coordinating with each other in both areas (see Fig. 273).

The Nail

The thumbs of such cases assume the form of a round ball, while their nails are even and flat. The nails look darkly

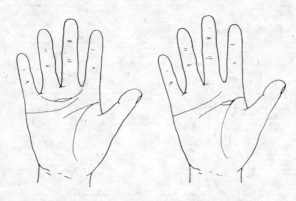

Fig. 270   Fig. 271

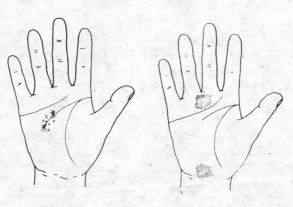

Fig. 272   Fig. 273

yellow and are free of any semilunar flaps (see Fig. 274).

The Tongue

The tongue looks darkly purple and is coated with thin and white or yellow and sticky fur. The sublingual vein becomes thicker and looks darkly purple.

The Neck

An enlarged thyroid may be palpated in the neck, and it does not move along with the action of swallowing. The pharynx looks relatively large.

The Facial Expression

The acupoint Yint'ang looks dark. The nose bridge is narrow, and, in contrast with the bulging eyes, presents a noticeable disharmony.

The Physical Form

Cases of hyperthyroidism have mostly an emaciated build.

The Ear

At the acupoint representing the servical vertebra on the ear, a chodral proliferation may be palpated (see Fig. 275).

Fig. 274   **Fig. 275**

Diabetes

Diabetes is a relatively common disease of the internal secretive metabolism. It is a generalized disease chiefly characterized by the disturbance of the carlohydrate metabolism caused by the absolute or relative insufficiency of insulin secretion and the weakened sensitivity of the target cells to the insulin. This disease often occurs among persons after their middle ages with a slightly higher rate of incidences among the male sex than among the female sex. In traditional Chinese medicine, it belongs to the category of diabetes.

1. Main Points for Diagnosis

a. Typical symptoms: thirstiness, insatiability, frequent urination, emciation and exhaustedness.

b. Positive reaction of the glucose in urine: fasting blood-glucose > 130 mg/dl and the blood-glucose 2 hours after meal > 200 mg/dl.

c. With a suspicious case, an OGTT is necessary. Of the four quartiles (the normal upper limit for the four quartiles is 30 minutes and 200 blood-glucose, and is indicated as: 30, 200; 60,190; 120,150; or 180,125 mg/dl), if three of them ⩾ the normal upper limit, then, the case can be identified as diabetes.

2. Clinical Types

a. The insulin-dependence type (Type I): this type of diabetes usually occurs among children and youths, and begins to attack rapidly and violently. It often shows distinct or severe symptoms such as desperate thirst, excessive water intake, frequent urination, emiciation and fatigue. The case often shows a tendency toward ketosis and even develops ketoacidosis. The secretive function of insulin is remarkably weakened, and when the glucose is loaded, there is still no distinct increase in the .concentration of the glucose. The patient's survival depends upon the insulin from an external source, and, generally, he or she is sensitive to the treatment with insulin.

b. The insulin-independence type (Type Ⅱ): this type of diabetes usually occurs among adults above 40 of age and elderly people, a larger number of whom have a fat build. It begins to attack slowly and shows only slight symptoms. Quite a few cases even do not show any symptoms of metabolistic disturbances, and will not develop ketosis under non-irritation conditions. As a rule, such cases indicate a normal level of plasma insulin, and that is why they do not rely on insulin in their treament. Sometimes, however, insulin is used with them in order to control the hyperglycemia and other pathologic changes. And quite often, such cases are not so sensitive to insulin.

3. Methods of Diagnosis

The Color and Luster of the Palm

a. The palm is scarlet red in color, and especially the scarlet red in the tips of the fingers are most attractive (see Fig. 276).

b. In the area designated as *Gen*, there is the presence of reticular contours of blood vessels, while in the areas designated as *Zhen* and *Qian* there is the presence of red small spots (see Fig. 277).

c. The scarlet red color under the ring finger refuses to disappear even if the finger is pressed (see Fig. 278).

d. The area designated as *Qian* bears a freshly red color with pale ring-like plaques.

The Palmar Line

a. In the area designated as *Qian*, there is a deep horizontal line which extends parallelly with the large thenar; if there are two such lines, it is more meaningful, and three of such lines may be observed on the palm of some cases of family heredity (see Fig. 279).

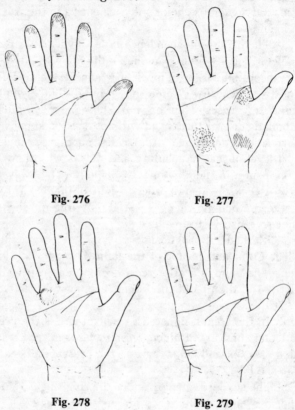

Fig. 276

Fig. 277

Fig. 278

Fig. 279

b. In the area designated as *Kan*, there are disordered lines (see Fig. 280).

c. Line 3 may be cut into by thin and small Line 6 (see Fig. 281).

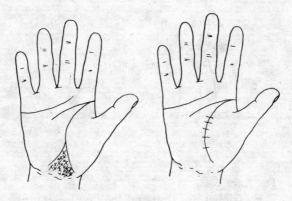

Fig. 280   **Fig. 281**

The Nail

Such patients often wear broad or hollow nails. With some cases, the hand as a whole becomes spoon-shaped (see Fig. 282), and it may viberates when put straightly forward. The roots of the nails often bear a light blue color, and, with the middle finger as the center, the other fingers tend to bend toward the thumb.

The Eye

Patients of diabetes are of acid constitutions. During the course of suffering from diabetes, the pupil on one side tends to look obliquely outward, mostly with the pupil of the left eye. The pupils are dilated and result in a dim and weakened eyesight (see Fig. 283).

Fig. 282   Fig. 283

The Ear

The earlobes are thin and look coffee-colored, or they often turn moistly red. They become reddish purple whenever they meet with cold. Besides, they are apt to get swollen, ulcerous and decrustatious.

The Tooth

The teeth are often become loose, there is often an infection in the gums, and a headache is a common occurrence.

The Facial Expression

Patients of diabetes usually wear a turbid and dark-colored face, and red spots may be observable along the edge of the hair at the rear head. Standing by the side of such a patient, one may smell an abnormal tart and stinky odor of the body.

The Physical Form

In the initial phase of the disease, fat builds are often

248

encountered, while in the advanced stage, emaciation is obvious. However, even when the patient is emaciated, he or she still retains a lot of fat in the abdomen which is usually prominently protruding. The limbs and the face are thin and feeble, and the hands and the feet are susceptible to numbness. Patients of diabetes are mostly fond of sleeping, and have very little saliva. Their skin is susceptible to furuncles, which are usually difficult to cure.

Rheumatoid Arthritis

Rheumatoid arthritis is a generalized disease chiefly characterized by chronic symmetrical and multiple arthritis. Its pathogenic factors remain unidentified, but it is generally believed that basically, the pathologic change in the articulations is generally caused by synovitis resulting from the autoimmune reaction after an infection. Adults between the ages of 20 and 40, with a larger proportion of the female sex, are susceptible to the disease. In traditional Chinese medicine, it belongs to the category of arthralgia-syndrome, migratory arthralgia and severe and migratory arthralgia.

1. Main Points for Diagnosis

a. The onset of the disease is slow, and before the presence of articular symptoms, there are general premonitory symptoms such as exhaustedness, low fever, poor appetite and coldness in the limbs.

b. The limbs bear symmetrical and multiple arthritis, with that of the small articulations of both hands (especially the proximal interphalangeal articulations of the hand) and that of the wrist, the knee and foot being most apparent. The proximal interphalangeal articulations appear in fusiforms, accompanied with pain, tenderness and stiffness, and finally result in the deviatory ulnar deformation and the atrophy of the adjacent muscles.

c. The subcutaneous nodules are mostly present at the prominent portions of the articulations, but they can also be found in the portions of the synovial bursa and the tendon sheath. The nodules vary in size, and their texture is as hard as rubber with slight tenderness and they exist persistently for a long time.

d. The active stage and remission stage emerge alternately.

e. During the active stage, the pace of blood consendimentation is accelerated, and the rheumatoid factors show a positive reaction.

f. The X-ray film of the articulations reveals signs of decalcification, osteoporosis, destruction of the bone, narrowed articular surface and joint fusion.

2. Clinical Types

a. The mild grade: there is no apparent deformity of the articulations, but the patient feels difficult in getting about. Physical labor is affected considerably.

b. The moderate grade: it is characterized by the deformity of the articulations and the loss of physical capability, but the patient can still take care of himself or herself.

c. The severe grade: it is characterized by apparent deformity of the articulations, and the patient has lost the capability to take care of himself or herself.

3. Methods of Diagnosis

The Finger

a. The proximal interphalangeal articutions are swollen in the fusiform, while the the interphalangeal articulations of the little finger are crooked and deformed.

b. The ulnar lateral of the metacarpophalangeal articulations appears deviatorily deformed and the interphalangeal articulations of the fingers are fixed at the crooked positions, so that the movement of the articulations of the fingers is restricted.

c. The sensation of the skin near the articulations is dulled, and the pathologically affected articulations become stiffened and crooked, so that they cannot meet the demand for the physiological activity (for all the above points, please see Fig. 284).

The Palmar Line

a. Both the large and small thenars are soft and plane.

b. At the lower end of Line 3 there is the presence of canopy-shaped lines (see Fig. 285).

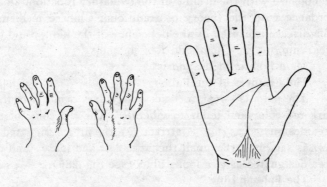

Fig. 284   Fig. 285

The Nose

The nose bridge becomes curved and gives a feeling of unevenness when palpated. The side it inclines to indicates that the articular deformity is more obvious on that side.

The Ear

There are noticeable uneven nodules at the acupoint representing the spine on the ear, and the ears are stiffened and can hardly be kneaded.

The Facial Expression

Such cases mostly wear a blue-pale complexion, and the blue color is particularly attractive around the mouth. They often look suffering.

Menopausal Syndrome

Menopausal syndrome refers to a syndrome which occurs among some women around their natural menopause. It is chiefly characterized by the biological changes and functional disturbances of the vegetative nerves caused by the menopause with the decline of the ovulatory function. In accordance with the theory of traditional Chinese medicine, this disease is caused by the deficiency of the kidney and the weakening of the *Chong* and *Ren* channels.

Main Points for Diagnosis

The Features of the Palm

The palm is sweaty or excessively dry, while it bears a dark red color and tends to viberate. The red color of the area designated as *Xun* is attractive, the area designated as *Kan* is sagging, the small thenar is soft and loose, and the area designated as *Gen* looks blue (see Fig. 286).

The Palmar Line

a. There is the formation of "△" —shaped lines on the outer side of the lower end of Line 3 (see Fig. 287).

b. There is a large "△" shape consisting of quite some thin, small and disordered lines on Line 2 (see again Fig. 287).

c. Line 2 may be terminated with insular lines (see Fig.

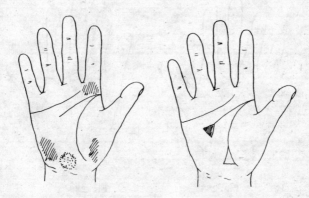

Fig. 286   **Fig. 287**

288).

d. From under the end of Line 5 there is a thin line which extends toward the little finger. This signifies that the person is fragile in temper, and is easy to get excited and depressed alternatively (see Fig. 289). Line 5 tends to become curved.

e. There is the presence of " * "-shaped lines on the second segment of the index finger (see Fig. 290).

The Tongue

The tongue fur is thin and pale, and the texture of the tongue often looks purple with ecchymosis, or the tip of the tongue looks red.

The Ear

There are visible contours of blood vessels in the cochlea (see Fig. 291).

The Facial Expression

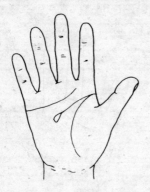

Fig. 288

Fig. 289

Fig. 290

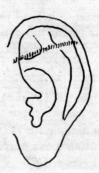

Fig. 291

254

Women who wear pigmentation spots on their faces usually show distinct symptoms of the syndrome. The larger such spots are in area and the deeper such spots are in color, the more indistinct the symptoms will be. The portions susceptible to pigmentation spots are shown in the following figure (see Fig. 292).

At the acupoint named Jenchung there is a vertical line, which extends itself to the nose. The point becomes shallower and flatter, and there is a visible blue color there (see Fig. 293).

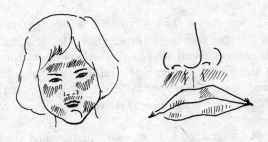

Fig. 292   **Fig. 293**

The Physical Form

Most of such cases have a pain in the heel, and with some severe cases, walking is impossible.

Neurosism

Neurosism is a common disease among those of neurosis. It results from the excitation and the dysfunction of the inhibition of the cerebrum and the weakening of the ability of psychomobility caused by various factors such as long-term excessive nervousness,overwork of the brain,irregulated life, etc. It usually occurs among youths and middle-aged persons. It is believed in traditional Chinese medicine that this disease has to do closely with the seven emotions (i. e. , joy, anger, melancholy, anxiety, fear, grief and terror) and the dysfunction of the heart and the liver.

1. Main Points for Diagnosis

a. Basic symptoms: sleeplessness, dreamfulness, dizziness and faint, declination of memory, inability to concentrate the mind, being easy to get anxious and angry, fear of sound and light, a ringing sound in the ear, a dim eyesight, and listlessness.

b. Symptoms of the dysfunction of the vegetative nerves and the internal organs: palpitation, a relatively high or low blood pressure, much sweating, a feeling of cold in the endings of the limbs, a feeling of swelling and distention in the upper abdomen,a poor appetite,constipation or diarrhea,and possible frequent urination, menoxnia, emission, or sexual impotence.

c. An examination of the case history and the systems cannot confirm the existence of any other related physical or psycho diseases.

d. The onset of this disease has to do clsoely with psycho factors.

e. The course of the disease shows a tendency toward recurrence, undulation and persistence, and its undulation is generally related with psycho factors.

2. Methods of Diagnosis

The Face

One who tends to suffer from neurosism usually wears

a "甲" -shaped face, i. e. , the parietal bone of the skull is so large that it is almost equal in area to half of the face. And the forehead is broad. The body is lean and the facial part seems to be particularly small as the huge head sits on a thin and long trunk. The chin is usually pointed, and there is a blue color under the eyes with slight puffiness in the eyelids.

The Hand

A case of neurosism usually suffers from dysfunction of the vegetative nerves, which are divided into the sympathetic nerve and the parasympathetic nerve. These two kinds of nerves play contrary roles and function antagonistically. The sympathetic nerve acts upon the skin of the external environments and plays the role of protection, attack and struggle, while the parasympathetic nerve is in charge of nutrition, generation and secretion of the human body, thus having the function to maintain the reproduction and multiplication of mankind. When the sympathetic nerve is excited, the body fluids become acidic, so that those who frequently get angry or weep tend to have acid body fluids. Reversely, joy, laughter and quiet repose will make the parasympathetic nerve excited, and it will result in base body fluids (see Table 1 and Table 2). Reversely, when the acid-base scale of the body fluids registers the value between pH 7. 2 and pH 7. 4, i. e. , when the sympathetic nerve and the parasympathetic nerve are in a state of antagonism, it signifies a fine health condition of the human body. The way to identify on the palm the excitation or repression of the sympathetic nerve and the parasympathetic nerve within the human body is as follows: first let the palms face downward and both of the arms stretch out horizontally to the left and right respectively, and then observe the features of the hand from different perspectives: with some cases, the lateral of the thumb in

257

front of the wrist may curve into a "$<$," with some cases, the hand bends outward (towards the lateral of the little finger) into a "$<$," while with other cases, the hand stretches straight forward without any crook. Those whose hands tend to curve toward the lateral of the thumb have relatively acid body fluids, those whose hands bend toward the lateral of the little finger usually have base body fluids, while those whose hands stretch out staightly forward have normal body fluids (see Fig. 294).

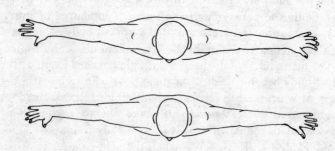

Fig. 294

Those who have broad spaces between their fingers when they put their fingers together tend to have excitation of the vagus nerve, while those who can put their fingers perfectly together without noticeable spaces tend to have excitation of the sympathetic nerve. Of all the fingers, the thumb has to do with the parasympathetic nerve, while all the other four fingers have to do with the sympathetic nerve.

One with a pointed chin usually has an unstable function of the nerves and therefore is susceptible to neurisism, especially one whose chin is not symmetrical with the upper and the middle sections of the face has a strong susceptibility to neurosism.

The acupoint Yint'ang bears a greenish pale color, and it indicates excessive fatigue and a severe case of neurosism.

The tips of the eyebrows of a male case of neurosism are straight and dry, while with a female case of such disease, it indicates that neurosism is complicated with abnormal menstruation.

The Palmar Line

In the light of the analysis by the palm, those whose acid area is larger than their base area have acid constitutions, and their sympathetic nerves are easy to be excited; while those whose base area is larger than their acid area mostly have base constitutions, and it shows the reservation of base of such persons. That Line 3 has become shallower signifies the insuficiency in the reservation of base within one's body and the existence of disease. The normal body fluids of healthy persons are of weak base, as most people have acid constitutions.

a. Line 3 is intercepted through by quite some Line 6 (see Fig. 295).

b. The palm bears a pale color.

c. There is the presence of disordered lines in the area designated as Li under the middle finger, or the muscles in that area are sagging and soft and loose, and there are visible contours of blood vessels (see Fig. 296).

d. Line 5 is tortuous and discontinuous and is cut through by Line 6.

e. At the end of Line 2 there is the formation of "△" - shaped or insular lines (see Fig. 297).

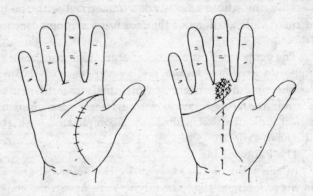

Fig. 295   **Fig. 296**

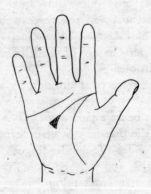

Fig. 297

Table 1　Excitation Conditions of the Sympathetic Nerves and the Parasympathetic Nerves and the Susceptive Diseases

nerve	body fluid	excitation condition	physical feature	susceptive disease
sympathetic nerve	acid	cold-water bath; spinal activity; getting angry; being nervous; weeping; sporting; meat-eating; descending a mountain	pupils enlarged; inward inclined eyeballs; thin and long body; narrow thorax	diabetes; hypertension; heart and kidney diseases; cerebral hemorrhage
para-sympathetic nerve	base	hot-water bath; abdominal activity; being joyous; stability in state of mind; laughing; being quiet; vegetable-eating; ascending a mountain	pupils contracted; outward inclined eyeballs; short and thick body; broad thorax	gastroxynsis; gastric ulcer; asthmoid convulsion; cancer

Table 2　Physical Features under the Excitation Conditions of the Sympathetic Nerves and the Parasympathetic Nerves

nerve	sympathetic nerve	parasympathetic nerve
body fluid	acid constitution	base constitution
skin color	rosy complexion	pale complexion
muscle	firm and strong	soft and feeble
build	the flat-plane type; limbs more developed than trunk	the shor-round type; trunk better developed than limbs
blood pressure	more cases of hypertension	more cases of hypotension
hair	more bald heads	hairs thick but apt to exfoliate
eyeball	inward oblique vision	outward oblique vision
pupil	large	small
finger	With the middle finger as the center, fingers tend to bend toward the thumb.	With the middle finger as the center, fingers bend toward the little finger.
falm	area encircled by Line 3 large	area encircled by Line 1 large
sports	feeling tired after sports	feeling more spirited after sports
secretion	little saliva, gastric fluid and sweat	excessive saliva, gastric fluid and sweat
sleep	sleeping a lot and somnolence	insomnia
temperament	impulsive, pugnacious and pessimistic	not bold enough, longing for tranquility, and pleasant

The Nail

The nails look pale and are free of any semilunar flaps. Mostly, they are thin and long nails (see Fig. 298).

The Tongue

The tongue may either be pale and lusterless with white fur or be red and dry without any fur. With some cases, their tongues viberate when put out.

The Tooth

There are loose teeth, frequent toothaches or infectious gums.

Fig. 298

The Eye

There are often red blood strings on the eyes, the eyelids are usually puffy, and those whose eyes look blue or dark in the edges are often cases accompanied with insomnia.

Ametropia

The dioptic system of the eye consists of the cornea, the aqueous humor, the crystal and the vitereous body and has a function of converging the light (focusing). The process of focusing of the parallel light through the flecxion of the dioptic system on the retina is known as the refraction of the eye. When the parallel light enters the eye in a still state of the eye, a vague image is produced due to the failure in its focusing on the retina, and this phenomenon is known as ametropia.

1. Clinical Types

Clinically, ametropia is divided into three types, i. e. , myopia, hyperopia and astigmatism.

a. Myopia: owing to the fact that the anteroposterior diameter of the eyeball is lengthened, when the eye is in its still state and the parallel light has entered, the focusing cannot be effected on the retina, and the imagery which takes place in front of the retina is known as nearsightedness. Such a case often has dim eyesight in looking at distant objects, but has a clear one when looking at objects at a short distance. With a severe case, the eye has to be narrowed in looking, or to see small things at a short distance, the target object must be put closely before the eye to improve the clarity.

b. Hyperopia: owing to the relative shortness of the anteroterior diameter of the eyeball, when the eye is in its still and the parallel light has entered, the imagery is effected behind the retina. Such a phenomenon is known as hyperopia. Such a case usually enjoys a clear vision in seeing distant objects while suffering a blurred vision in seeing small objects or even written words right in front of the eye. Now and then, he or she may suffer visual fatigue. A severe case may suffer a blurred vision for both distant and close objects, and is often accompanied with a pain in the eyeball, headache and a sense of glabellar weightiness.

c. Astigmatism: due to the abnormal of the curvature of the surface of the cornea, when the eye is in its still state and the parallel light has entered, the focusing cannot be effected on the retina and the imagery is vague. Such a phenomenon is known as astigmatism. The patient usually has a sense of vagueness in vision when looking at objects both distant and close before the eye. A severe case may suffer visual fatigue, headache and an aching pain in the eyeball.

2. Methods of Diagnosis

The Palm

a. The presence of a dim and dark-gray semicircular line at the root of the middle finger generally indicates myopia, which tends to be of family heredity (see Fig. 299).

b. There are thin and small insular lines on Line 1 under the ring finger (see Fig. 299).

c. There is the presence of thin and small insular lines at conjunctive point of Line 2 and Line 3 (see Fig. 300).

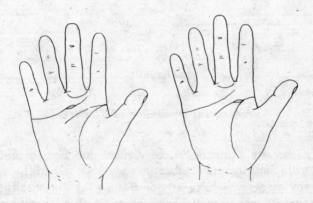

Fig. 299   Fig. 300

d. Both laterals of the root of the middle finger bear a dark blue color, and the chromatism of the color on both laterals indicates the inequality in the visual acuity of the two eyes: the heavier the color is, the poorer the vision will be. That in the radial surface represents the left eye, while that in the ulnar surface, the right eye (see Fig. 301).

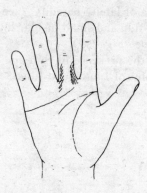

Fig. 301

A General Discussion of Tumors

Generally, tumors can be divided into benign tumors and malignant tumors. Tumor, as a whole, is one of the most servere diseases which are pernicious to the health of mankind. Cases of malignant tumors, with a low cure rate and a high mortality rate, often occur among persons in or after their middle ages. Commonly encountered malignant tumors chiefly include the carcinoma of the cervix, the mammary cancer, the carcinoma of the stomach, the carcinoma of the esphagus, the nasopharyneal carcinoma, the colon-rectal carcinoma, the hepatocarcinoma, the oral carcinoma, the pulmonary carcinoma and the skin carcinoma, which constitute a percentage of 75 of all the cases of malignant tumors. Owing to the limitations of the current medical treatment and other conditions, regular and overall physical examinations cannot yet be carried out universally so as to discover cases of tumors premonitarily. Therefore, it has become significant to popularize some simple and practical methods of diagnosis by observing the skin and physical features so that such cases may be found out in their initial stage. The authoress of this book, based upon her clinical practice, has epitomized the following methods for the earlier diagnosis of tumors.

The Color and Luster of the Palm

The palm bears a color of dark blue or withered yellow, with brown, white or dark red spots. In accordance with the locations of the spots, the pathogenetic internal organs may be judged respectively.

The Palmar Line

a. There are few lines on the palm, except for the three main lines accompanied with a deep Line 4 and the dividing line between the areas designated as *Gen* and *Zhen*, thus forming a "Five-lined Palm. " This feature generally signifies the existence of tumor in the digestive system. And at the same time, it indicates that such a tumor has a family history (see Fig. 302).

b. There is the formation of Line 13 on both palms. Mostly, this feature signifies the possible occurrence of a malignant disease in the blood circulatory system (see Fig. 303).

c. Line 3 is cut short or has insular lines at its ending (see Fig. 304).

d. There are insular lines at the middle section and the ending section of Line 2 (see Fig. 305).

e. There are insular lines at the middle section of Line 1 (see Fig. 306).

f. There are insular lines on Line 4 or at the conjunctive

position of Line 4 and Line 3 (see Fig. 307).

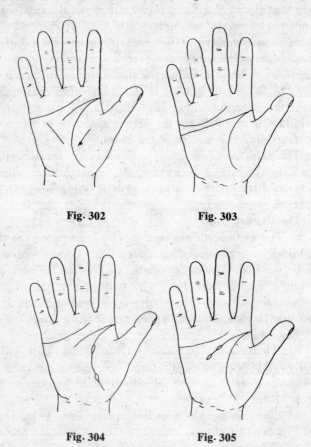

Fig. 302   Fig. 303

Fig. 304   Fig. 305

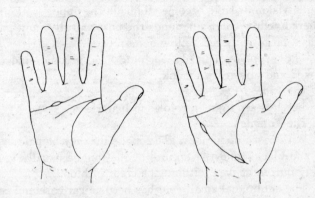

Fig. 306   **Fig. 307**

The presence of insular lines at the middle sections of the lines generally indicates the existence of the tumor in the middle part of the human body, while that at the ending sections indicates the pathologic change in the lower abdomen.

The Nail

The semilunar flaps have disappeared, the roots of the nails bear a color of withered yellow, onychoptosis has occurred or the nails have become barrel-shaped.

The muscles of the finger tips are wrapped up by the edges of the nails. If the nails have become "small nails," it usually indicates the existence of tumor in the digestive system; if they have become "long nails," it usually indicates the existence of tumor in the respiratory system; unevenness of the nail surface, difference of the subungual color with checkered dark and pale colors both show the features of the existence of tumors.

The Facial Expression

The complexion of a case of tumor is often covered with a dark blue hue. The eyes usually assume an outward oblique vision or have become albinic in the upper section. A withered yellow color surrounds the nose and the mouth and forms a large withered yellow delta area.

The acupoint named Jenchung has become uneven, crooked and upwardly shrunk.

The Lip

The lips are light in color and lusterless.

The Tongue

With cases of tumors, the tongue fur may be pale, yellow and black, and the texture of the tongue usually looks darkly purple or pale without the color of blood.

The sublingual small vein has become varicose and congestive, and appears in a reticular form, with brown spots at the endings of the blood vessels. The sublingual mucosa as a whole is enveloped with a misty white-blue color, and that mostly indicates the existence of tumors in the stomach or the intestinal tract. The presence of jaundice in the sublingual may signify the existence of tumor in the liver system. A distinctly bulging and purple-blue sublingual vein may suggest the existence of tumor in the lungs.

中国掌纹诊病

原著　王晨霞

绘图　大升　芙蓉

翻译　老安　王渤

　　　李彦文　赵秀风

校译　安增才

*

中国山东友谊出版社出版

（地址：中国山东济南胜利大街 39 号　邮编：250001）

中国山东人民印刷厂印刷

中国国际图书贸易总公司发行

（中国北京车公庄西路 35 号）

北京邮政信箱第 399 号　邮政编码　100044

英文版

1996 年 3 月第 1 版　　1996 年 3 月第 1 次印刷

ISBN 7—80551—768—1/R·11

05800

14—E—3038P